Take Two

Duologues for Young Players

Chosen by
Anne Harvey

Samuel French–London
New York – Sydney – Toronto – Hollywood

© 1981 by Samuel French Ltd

ISBN 0 573 19027 5

CONTENTS

DUOLOGUES FOR TWO BOYS

DUOLOGUES FOR TWO GIRLS

DUOLOGUES FOR ONE BOY AND ONE GIRL

AUTHOR'S INDEX

FOREWORD

Forewords to practical books like this one tend to be an unknown quantity. The readers are far more likely to want to move on to the contents and to start acting. However, if you've got time I hope you'll spend a few minutes on this part.

This collection has been interesting and rewarding to compile. My own students, those intrepid "guinea pigs" of Notting Hill and Ealing High School, have helped me by trying the scenes out, and you'll see that I have widened the scope by including extracts from TV Scripts and novels as well as plays. I hope that anyone using this book will be alert to the possibilities there are in literature and will go on searching for more material. There is always room for new ideas. Remember, though, that you MUST ask permission any time that you want to use an extract. Write to the publisher in the first instance, and he will advise you.

The duologues can be used for classwork as well as performance. For example:

A group of five could be producer, actors, stage manager and critic during one drama lesson.

Some of the scenes offer a talking point and could lead to group discussion.

Most schools and many individuals now have tape or cassette recorders. These can be most valuable in simulating a broadcasting situation. A group could include actors, producer, perhaps a narrator to explain the action, and a "sound effects" person.

Some of the scenes might lend themselves to an improvisation exercise. You could read the scene through, and then develop ideas for a follow-up, or preceding dialogue, perhaps involving other characters. Or, as an experiment, change the period or setting of a scene. Put a modern scene back in time or update a period piece. Imaginative ways of handling the material can only enhance your understanding.

Several Examination Boards offer chances for duologue acting, and of course the Duologue class is still one of the most popular in Speech and Drama Festivals. When I travel about the country examining and adjudicating I am always asked for new ideas so I hope that you will find enough variety here for all sorts of events and occasions.

Lastly, two pieces of advice:

Choose your scene wisely. While it is interesting and necessary to experiment in class, for performance you must be convincing. If you are plump and hearty you may not be at your best cast as a fairy. If you are very feminine and light voiced you may not make a good man! Of course in acting there are no rules and I have seen excellent playing from unexpected players. But you must learn to know yourself, and discover what you can achieve without self-consciousness.

Do try to read the whole book or play. This is one of my pet nags! It is not very intelligent, or fair to yourself, your audience, or the author to attempt an extract without more idea of character and situation than the piece shows. You will only have yourself to blame if you do not "do your homework". In cases where I think it might be difficult to obtain the whole book I have given a full synopsis to help you.

Duologues can be immensely rewarding. From a short scene you can learn a great deal about playing together, pace, reaction, timing, character development, movement and setting.

I hope you will enjoy acting these duologues as much as I have enjoyed choosing them.

ANNE HARVEY

ACKNOWLEDGEMENTS

For permission to print or reprint copyright extracts from copyright works in this volume the compiler and publishers are grateful to the following authors, translators, their representatives and publishers:

Louisa Alcott: (from *Little Women*, Combridge Jackson Ltd) the adapter, Sheila Corbett and the Publishers

Shankara Angadi: (from *Night Child*, unpublished) the Author

Nina Bawden: (from *The Witch's Daughter*, Gollancz Ltd) the Author, the Publishers and Curtis Brown Ltd

Mary Haley Bell: (from *Far Morning*, William Heinemann Ltd) the Author, the Publishers and Laurence Pollinger Ltd

Robert Bolt: (from *The Thwarting of Baron Bolligrew*, Samuel French Ltd) the Author

Pamela Brown: (from *Maddy Alone*, Hutchinson Publishing Group Ltd) the Author and the Publishers, to whom application must be made for public performance

Anthony Buckeridge: (from *Jennings and Darbishire*, William Collins) the Author and the Publishers

K. & C. Capek: (from *The Insect Play*, Oxford University Press) the Translator, Paul Selver and the Publishers

Aidan Chambers: (from *The Car*, Heinemann Educational Books) the Author and the Publishers

Charlotte Chorpenning: (from *Radio Rescue*, J. Garnet Miller) the Author and the Publishers

Hilary Clulow: (from *Treasure Quest*, unpublished) the Author

Helen Cresswell: (from *Lizzie Dripping*, Jackanory Story Books, BBC) the Author, the Publishers and A. M. Heath & Co Ltd

Roald Dahl: (from *James and the Giant Peach*, George Allen and Unwin) the Author, and the Publishers

David Scott Daniell: (from *The Stowaway*, Harrap, and *The King's Messenger*, Harrap) the Publishers and David Higham Associates Ltd

Eleanor Farjeon: (from *And I Dance Mine Own Child*) David Higham Associates Ltd; (from *The Silver Curlew*, Samuel French Ltd) the Publishers

Henri Gheon: (from *Christmas In The Market Place*, J. Garnet Miller) the Translator, Eric Crozier, and the Publishers

Margaret Gibbs: (from *The Flibberty Fly-By-Night*, Heinemann Educational Books) the Author and the Publishers; (from *The Treasure In The Witchball*, unpublished) the Author

Rumer Godden: (from *The Dolls House*, Macmillan, London and Basingstoke) the Author and the Publishers; (from *The River*, Macmillan, London and Basingstoke) the Author, the Publishers and Curtis Brown Ltd

Nicholas Stuart Gray: (from *New Lamps For Old*, Dennis Dobson) the Publishers; (from *The Princess and the Swineherd*, Dennis Dobson) the Publishers; (from *Gawain and the Green Knight*, Dennis Dobson) the Publishers. Application for public performance should be made to English Theatre Guild Ltd

Margaret Greaves: (from *The Grandmother Stone*, Methuen Children's Books Ltd) the Author and the Publishers

L. P. Hartley: (from *The Shrimp and the Anemone*, from a trilogy, *Eustace and Hilda*, Putnam and Co Ltd) the Publishers

Lillian Hellman: (from *The Children's Hour*, Dramatists Play Service). Copyright 1934 by Lillian Hellman, renewed 1961 by Lillian Hellman. Reprinted by permission of the Harold Matson Company Inc

A. P. Herbert: (from *Fat King Melon*, Oxford University Press) the Publishers

Susan Hill: (from *I'm The King of the Castle*, Hamish Hamilton Ltd) the Author and the Publishers; (from *Lizard In The Grass*, BBC Publications) the Author and Richard Scott Simon Ltd

Jackson Lacy: (from *The Prince, The Wolf and The Firebird*, Calder and Boyars) the Unicorn Theatre, London WC2

A Lintern: (from *The Goose Girl*, Pitman Publishing Ltd) the Publishers

Nikki Marvin: (from *The Legend of Scarface and Blue Water*, Methuen) Blanche Marvin, 21a, St John's Wood High Street, NW8

James McTaggart: (from *Boys and Girls Come Out to Play*, unpublished) Goodwin Associates and the Executors to the Estate of James McTaggart

Helen Murdoch: (from *Alan and the King's Daughters*, Samuel French Ltd) the Author and the Publishers

Eric Newton and Jean McDonnell: (from *The Legend of Carcassone*, University of London Press) the Authors

Bill Owen: (from *The Ragged School*, Macmillan Dramascript) the Author, the Editor, Guy Williams, and the Publishers

Philippa Pearce: (from *Minnow on the Say*, Oxford University Press) the Author and the Publishers; (from *Tom's Midnight Garden*, Oxford University Press) the Author and the Publishers

K. M. Peyton: (from *Flambards*, Oxford University Press) the Author and the Publishers

Antonia Ridge: (from *How Jan Klaassen Cured The King*, Faber & Faber Ltd) the Author and the Publishers

Joan Robinson: (from *When Marnie Was There*, Collins) the Author and the Publishers

David Rowley: (from *In Need of Care*, Samuel French Ltd) the Author and the Publishers; (from *Gone Away To Work*, unpublished) the Author

Ivan Southall: (from *Josh*, Angus and Robertson (UK) Ltd) the Publishers

Catherine Storr: (from *Thursday*, Faber & Faber Ltd) the Publishers

Peter Terson: (from *Zigger Zagger*, Penguin Books Ltd). Copyright Peter Terson, 1970. Reprinted by permission of Penguin Books Ltd

Nora Tully: (from *Titian*, Dennis Dobson) the Publishers

Tennessee Williams: (from *Summer and Smoke*, published in *Four Plays*

By Tennessee Williams, Secker & Warburg).Copyright 1951 by Tennessee
Williams. Reprinted by permission of the Author and his Agent,
Elaine Greene Ltd
David Wood: (from *Flibberty and the Penguin*, Samuel French Ltd) the
Author and the Publishers
David Wood and Sheila Ruskin: (from *The Owl and the Pussycat Went to
See* . . ., Samuel French Ltd) the Authors and the Publishers
Arthur Wise: (from *The Naughty Girls*) the Author

THE FAR MORNING

JO / RED

You will be fortunate if you can find a copy of this fascinating book, part of which involves a dream sequence. In this extract Red, a small boy whose father owns a large country estate, does not know that his dog has been killed in an accident. While he is searching he meets Jo, a shepherd's son, who saw it happen

Red (*off, calling*) Hamlet! Hamlet! . . . Hamlet . . . Hamlet . . .

He enters, half-asleep, clutching a bunch of foxgloves and wheat

(*Wearily*) Hamlet . . . Hamlet . . .

There is no reply. He sighs deeply, and something seems to stop him calling. Jo is there

Jo H'lo Red . . .
Red H'lo Jo . . .
Jo What you been doin' then? Been asleep?
Red (*nodding*) I been running so much I got tired . . .
Jo Running . . . ?
Red Looking for Hamlet . . .
Jo (*his eyes widening*) Hamlet . . . ?
Red Have you seen him?
Jo (*shuffling in the grass*) Not since this morning . . .
Red I can't find him.
Jo (*giving him a long straight look*) You won't find him neither.
Red Of course I will.
Jo 'Course you won't . . .
Red Why not?
Jo He's dead, is Hamlet.
Red (*his eyes blazing*) Dead?
Jo (*too late now, he's broken the news*) Yes. . . . He's dead.
Red (*unbelieving*) 'Course he's not dead. . . . How do you know he's dead?
Jo I saw him dead.
Red (*quite still*) You . . . saw?
Jo (*not liking this*) Sure.
Red Where?
Jo In the road.
Red What road?
Jo Outside of our 'ouse . . .
Red Oh no . . .
Jo I'm sorry . . .
Red How was he dead?

1

Jo Runned over by a lorry.
Red It was a rabbit!
Jo No, it was Hamlet.
Red He couldn't be . . . he couldn't be run over by a lorry.
Jo He was I tell you. I see 'un. . . . Any dog can be. Ask Harold. Ask my old man . . .
Red I don't want to. . . . Does my mother know?
Jo 'Course. Everyone knows. . . . It's bad luck, that's what it is . . .

Red stands his ground with dignity, but his world has collapsed. His friend killed, he is utterly alone . . . he slashes at the long grass

Red Well. . . . (*His voice cracks . . . he clears his throat*) Where is he now then?
Jo Under the poplars by the tennis court.
Red Why?
Jo Dunno. Heard your father tell my old man. "He's an old friend," he said, "he deserves a place on the farm."
Red Yes.
Jo This sodden lorry nearly went through our house. . . . Your father has his number . . .
Red Under the poplars . . .
Jo (*glad Red is taking it all so well*) That's right.
Red Jo. . . . What is it to be dead, Jo?
Jo (*shuffling*) Dunno rightly. In Sunday School they make it all right.
Red How?
Jo Sleep, they say, don't they? (*He turns away, remembering the accident, which had made him feel sick; he'd run to his mother. He sniffs*) Think I gotta cold.
Red Or hay-fever.
Jo Yes, that's it. Hay-fever.

There is a pause

Red (*quietly*) What kind of a lorry?
Jo It had wrote on the back . . . "Rely on us."
Red Rely on us . . . (*He listens, a barking sound*) There's a dog-fox out there . . .
Jo In the barley . . .
Red (*picking up his flowers*) Think I'll go home now.
Jo Me too.
Red Goodnight Jo.

They separate. Jo is crying silently. After a moment Red looks at the sky

(*Whispering*) Hamlet. (*Shouting*) Hamlet!

Adapted from MARY HALEY BELL

GAWAIN AND THE GREEN KNIGHT

GAWAIN / GREEN KNIGHT

Based on the Middle English poem and the ancient legend of the Loathly Lady. Gawain of Orkney keeps his promise to meet the Green Knight a year after striking off the Knight's head. Unknown to him the Knight is Sir Bercilak at whose castle he has had hospitality. Gawain's problem is his endless war with himself. His terrible mother has sapped his confidence and he is always on the defensive. In this first scene she manages to telephone him in an unusual way. The play is set loosely around AD 500

As the scene opens Gawain is on stage. A sound makes him swing round quickly. It is the sound of an axe being sharpened. He listens for a few moments

Gawain (*calling loudly*) If that's your greeting to me, you've made your effect! Now show yourself, if you're the one I've come to meet. This is Gawain of Orkney.

The noise continues. Gawain moves forward a little

It's a cold place here, to stand waiting—and listening. And unmannerly in you to keep me so. It's close on midnight. I've kept my word. Are you for breaking yours?

The honing stops. Through the mist, the Green Knight comes striding. His head is back on his neck, and he comes to a halt and looks at Gawain with glowing red eyes. A pause. Gawain, with an effort, goes on speaking

I—don't care over much for your Chapel. A hollow barrow—a grave-mound. Only fitted for unholy rites. And a bitter wind blowing from it. Do you mean to make me go in there?

Knight This open ground will serve. Welcome, sir. I trust you recollect the purpose of our meeting?

Gawain It's not a thing that slips the memory.

The Knight runs his thumb down the blade of the axe

Knight Come, then. This mist may blunt the blade. Finish the game now

Gawain As quickly as you will. (*He leans his sword against a tree, and goes towards the Knight, pushing back his mail hood from his neck*)

Knight No need for that, sir. My axe will cut through armour as swiftly as it slices flesh and bone. One blow is all my due, and—

Gawain And one will suffice.

He is about to kneel, when a thin whistling comes from one of the sheep-skulls

I'm not answering that!

3

Knight Not even to say farewell?

Gawain hesitates. Then he goes to the skull, and speaks close to it, with miserable anger. It twitters in reply a few times

Gawain It's Gawain, and I don't want to talk just now. Oh, I'm sorry, then! But I—mother, I'm busy. Just for once, will you leave me alone! I am not living a life of dissolute pleasure! Mother, I'm in a bit of a hurry. I—mother, could you not for once just say good-bye, in a kind sort of way? Yes, maybe I am absurd, but—

The twittering stops abruptly. Gawain looks at the skull bitterly

Och, she might have—just this time—

He breaks off, and stalks back to the Knight

I hope you had a human mother, sir!
Knight Well—

But Gawain has not realized the implication of what he has said. He kneels, in a rage of hurt dignity

Gawain Take your blow, and let me be done with it all.

The Knight slowly lifts the axe above his shoulder, and Gawain bends his head

Knight I will take only my right, sir.

He brings the axe down fast, but stops just before he touches Gawain, who has jerked his head aside. The Knight speaks with grave reproach

You flinched with fear before you felt the stroke. I never did so, when I knelt for yours.
Gawain My head is not replaceable. I should not have moved, and will not do so again. Finish it now!

Again the Knight swings up the axe, and again as it descends, he halts the blow. Gawain looks up at him crossly

Why do you hesitate?
Knight To see if you stayed still.
Gawain I did so! You dawdle overlong. I might die of boredom!
Knight Not you, Gawain.

He swings his axe a third time. He halts it, and then drops it on Gawain's neck, just hard enough to wound him slightly. The Knight raises the axe, and waits, with the haft resting across his shoulder. After feeling the blow, Gawain puts a hand to the back of his neck, looks at the blood on his fingers, and jumps to his feet. He backs to the thorn-bush and takes up his sword

Gawain You've taken your return stroke. If you want more, I'm not called on to submit unresisting.

The Knight leans on his axe, and laughs

Knight Sheath your sword. I've no quarrel with you, sir. If I wished to see your head on the ground, I could have put it there.

Gawain Why didn't you?

Knight Measure for measure Gawain. At my castle, for three days you played fairly, giving me the prizes that you won. I held back the first axe-stroke—not only because you shrank from it, but for my wife's kiss that you repaid to me. The second for the second. And the third—

Gawain (*under his breath*) You are Bercilak?

Knight The people of the Hills have many shapes. Even the third blow was not struck to kill. If I could, I would have spared you that small wound. We tested you in many ways, and almost you won through in perfect honour. But—somewhat you flagged, sir. In just one thing you failed. And the green ribbon on your shoulder cost you the gash you bear.

Understanding, Gawain finds the knowledge bitter. He pulls off the ribbon, and drops it on the ground

Too late, Orkney.

Gawain All the time—you waited all the time for me to lie to you. And at the last, I lied.

Knight For fear of death. A less worthy lie would have cost you your head. There is no power at all in that ribbon. It was only part of a test.

Gawain I've done well. I kept the ribbon from you. I couldn't bide the fall of the axe. There's nothing to say. Let me go now.

Knight Try to forgive me and yourself.

Gawain I'm not a forgiving person. Now—my brother will be waiting—

Knight He is not.

Gawain (*not heeding this remark*) And the king—the king will be wanting to hear how my journeying ended.

He starts to move down right, and suddenly stops, and looks at the other

Why did you do it? I took your challenge. Couldn't you be content to strike your proper blow?

Knight Orkney, I have been under enchantment. Unless a man was bold enough to submit to the axe—and honest enough to escape with his life— I must have kept this guise from time to time, forever. Be content with your victory in this, at least.

Gawain goes and picks up the ribbon

Gawain You said I could keep this. So I will. And wear it always, plain to see. To remind me. For fear I might deceive myself into some pride again.

He turns away, and pauses as the Knight's next words halt him

Knight What are you going to do?

Gawain Return to the king. Tell him—and everyone—what I've done here. If they also make excuses for me, I know fine where I can go to hear the truth. Where I'd thought never to run again!

Knight You mean to pull your whole life down about your head?

Gawain goes to the trees, down R, *and pauses. He says, without turning and without emotion*

Gawain Thank you for your hospitality. Commend me to your lady.

He goes out

The Knight stands with hands folded on the head of the axe, looking after him

Knight A frame of mind to lose everything for us all. But spur as fast as you may, my friend, I know another road.

NICHOLAS STUART GRAY

I'M THE KING OF THE CASTLE

HOOPER/KINGSHAW

Edmund Hooper and Charles Kingshaw, both aged eleven, are thrown together when Mrs Kingshaw becomes the Hoopers' housekeeper. The two widowed parents felt this a good idea, expecting the boys to become friends. But from the start Hooper, hard and rather insensitive, part bully, part coward, and the far more vulnerable Kingshaw dislike each other intensely. Kingshaw decides to run away, but Hooper finds him, in the wood

Hooper Kingshaw, it's getting dark.

Kingshaw I know.

Hooper What time is it?

Kingshaw You ought to have a watch of your own. I'm fed up with telling you the time.

Hooper My father's going to buy me a new one this Christmas, he's going to give me a gold watch anyway, with a date on, and Roman numbers you can see in the dark. It'll cost a lot of money. About fifty pounds I should think, MORE than fifty pounds.

Kingshaw Liar, no watch costs that much.

Hooper They do, they do. They can cost hundreds and hundreds of pounds, sometimes. You don't know anything about anything.

Kingshaw Nobody's father would buy them a watch that cost fifty pounds.

Hooper My father would, because I'm the most important thing he's got in his whole life, he said ... so he'd buy me anything I wanted. ... Anyway, what time is it?

Kingshaw Gone eight o'clock. Twenty past eight, nearly. (*He scratches his head*)

Hooper You've got nits.

Kingshaw It's midge bites.

Hooper If you make the fire a lot bigger they'll go off. Midges don't like fire.

Kingshaw No, it's the smoke, it kills them.

Hooper It doesn't kill them, they just don't like it, so they go away.

Kingshaw Yes, it does kill them. You can see them dropping in. They get suffocated.

Hooper The moths will come as well.

Kingshaw Stuff it. We've got enough to think about.

Hooper If one little moth came and crawled on you, you'd pee your pants.

Kingshaw I said stuff it.

Hooper Scaredy-baby.

Kingshaw Shut up.

Hooper Are you?

Kingshaw What?

7

Hooper Scared?

Kingshaw (*warily*) What of?

Hooper Anything . . . of when it gets dark.

Kingshaw No. . . . That bump's swollen on your head. It's gone all black.

Hooper That's your fault.

Kingshaw Don't be stupid. Does it still hurt?

Hooper I might have been dead because you went off and left me, and if I had been dead, you'd have been a murderer; you shouldn't have gone into the wood by yourself.

Kingshaw Oh, shut up, you're not dead. You've only banged yourself.

Hooper You're a bully. You're supposed to be looking after me, because I hurt myself.

Kingshaw Baby-baby-Hooper!

Hooper You wait . . . you wait . . .

There is a pause

Kingshaw Tomorrow we've got to have rations. I'll divide all the food up. It won't last for very long.

Hooper Then what'll happen?

Kingshaw We'll have got out by then.

Hooper What if we don't?

Kingshaw We WILL have.

Hooper I wish we hadn't ever come in here anyway.

Kingshaw You didn't have to, you just followed me.

Hooper It was you that got us lost.

Kingshaw No, it was not so, it was you that started running about like a stupid fool.

There is a pause

Hooper They'll be coming home now . . . they'll be on the train.

Kingshaw I suppose so.

Hooper Soon, they'll start looking for us.

Kingshaw No they won't. Not tonight anyway.

Hooper Of course they will . . . why won't they?

Kingshaw Because how will they know we're not in bed? If they don't get back till late they won't even bother to look.

Hooper There's Mrs Boland and she'll tell them.

Kingshaw No. She goes at four o'clock. She'd think we'd just gone for a picnic or something, she never bothers. Nobody will know.

Hooper Your mother goes upstairs to see you. I know because I hear her. She has to kiss you goodnight like a little baby.

Kingshaw Boil your head. She doesn't always come.

Hooper Yes, she does, then. Kiss, kiss, kiss. Oh there, my little darling, dear little baby boy. Mummy loves her little baby-boy. Mummy goes cuddle, cuddle, cuddle every night. . . . Little diddums-baby, that's what!

Kingshaw Just because you haven't got a mother at all.

Hooper I wouldn't want one.

Kingshaw That's a stupid thing to say.

Hooper Fathers are better. Anybody who hasn't got a father is useless . . . you'd better not try and hit me.

Kingshaw If you don't want to catch fire, you'd better move back out of the way . . .

Hooper Has your mother gone after a lot of people?

Kingshaw What do you mean?

Hooper I mean, like she's gone after my father, that's why you came here. You didn't think it was for anything else did you? She wants to be married to my father. He's rich.

Kingshaw Liar, liar, liar. Your father isn't anything. She doesn't even LIKE your father. She hates him.

Hooper There are things I see that you don't.

Kingshaw What? What things?

Hooper Never mind. But you've got to believe me.

Kingshaw Your father's nothing.

Hooper Look, it's all right, Kingshaw. It's only what ladies do. If she hasn't got a husband, she's got to find one.

Kingshaw Why has she?

Hooper Well, because he'd give her money and a house and things. That's what always happens. . . . There are things I see that you don't.

SUSAN HILL

JAMES AND THE GIANT PEACH

SPONGE / SPIKER

James lives with his two unpleasant aunts, Sponge and Spiker. Their names give you a clue to their character and appearance, but you can find the illustrations and read about them in the popular book. I see no reason why two boys should not enjoy an attempt at these two characters . . .

Scene: In the garden

Spiker (*shouting*) Sponge . . . Sponge . . . Come here at once and look at this.
Sponge At what?
Spiker (*shouting*) It's a peach.
Sponge A what?
Spiker A peach . . . right up there on the highest branch. Can't you see it?
Sponge I think you must be mistaken, my dear Spiker. That miserable tree *never* has any peaches on it.
Spiker There's one on it now, Sponge. You look for yourself.
Sponge You're teasing me, Spiker. You're making my mouth water on purpose when there's nothing to put into it. Why, that tree's never even had a *blossom* on it, let alone a peach. Right up on the highest branch, you say? I can't see a thing. Very funny . . . Ha, ha. . . . GOOD GRACIOUS me! Well, I'LL BE BLOWED! There really IS a peach up there!
Spiker A nice big one too.
Sponge A beauty, a beauty!

There is a pause

Spiker (*breaking the silence*) It looks ripe to me.
Sponge (*licking her thick lips*) Then why don't we eat it? We can have half each . . . James must be made to climb the tree and pick it . . . Ja . . .
Spiker (*quickly, before she can say his name*) Stop! Hold everything . . . (*Staring up, mouth open, eyes bulging*) LOOK . . . LOOK, Sponge, LOOK!
Sponge What's the matter with you?
Spiker It's growing. . . . It's getting bigger and bigger.
Sponge What is?
Spiker The peach, of course.
Sponge You're joking!
Spiker Well, look for yourself!
Sponge But my dear Spiker, that's perfectly ridiculous. That's impossible. That's—that's—that's—Now, wait JUST a minute—No—No—that can't be right—No—Yes—Great Scott! The thing really IS growing!
Spiker (*shouting*) It's nearly twice as big already.

10

Sponge It can't be true.
Spiker It IS true.
Sponge It must be a miracle.
Spiker Watch it . . . watch it . . .
Sponge I am watching it.
Spiker (*yelling*) Great Heavens alive! I can actually see the thing bulging and swelling before my very eyes.
Sponge It's the size of a melon!
Spiker Just look at it growing. . . . It's twice as big again.
Sponge (*waving fat arms and dancing in circles*) Will it ever stop?
Spiker Keep away from the trunk . . . the slightest shake and I'm sure it'll fall off. It must weigh twenty or thirty pounds at least.
Sponge Stand back. It's coming down . . . the branch is going to break.
Spiker It has to stop now . . . it's as big as you, Sponge. It can't go on forever.
Sponge It's not stopping. It's the size of a small car . . .

Both aunts begin hopping around, shouting and clapping

Spiker Hallelujah! What a peach! What a peach!
Sponge Terrifico! Magnifico! Splendifico! And what a meal!
Spiker It's still growing!
Sponge I know, I know . . .
Spiker Look . . . it's growing faster and faster now . . . it's speeding up.
Sponge I see it, Spiker . . . I do . . . I do . . .
Spiker It's as big as a small house. . . . Ah, it's reached the ground . . .
Sponge It—can't fall off now.
Spiker It's stopped growing.
Sponge No, it hasn't.
Spiker Yes, it has!
Sponge It's slowing down, Spiker, it's slowing down. But it hasn't stopped yet. You watch it . . .!
Spiker It has now.
Spiker I believe you're right.
Sponge Do you think it's safe to touch it?
Spiker I don't know. We'd better be careful.

The Aunts walk slowly around the giant peach, inspecting it. They look like midgets

Sponge (*advancing cautiously, touching it with one finger tip*) It's ripe! It's just perfect! Now, look here, Spiker. Why don't we go and get a shovel right away and dig out a great big chunk of it for you and me to eat?
Spiker No, not yet.
Sponge Why ever not?
Spiker Because I say so.
Sponge (*her mouth is watering now*) But I can't WAIT to eat some . . .
Spiker (*with a thin lipped smile*) My dear Sponge. . . . (*She winks at her sister*) There's a pile of money to be made out of this if only we can handle it right. You wait and see.

ROALD DAHL

JENNINGS AND DARBISHIRE

JENNINGS / DARBISHIRE

Jennings and Darbishire have started a magazine at Linbury Court Preparatory School and have offered sponge cakes as prizes in 2 competitions. As with all their ideas things do not turn out simply . . .

Jennings I can't think what's come over Aunt Angela. It's over a week since I wrote and asked for those double-deckers. Mind you, I know she's as absent-minded as two coots, but you would think she'd try to remember, especially as I went to the trouble of underlining it in red ink.

Darbishire People who are like that ought to do something about it . . . like, say, for instance, tying knots in bits of string, so it reminds them to remember not to forget things.

Jennings You'd need something better than a bit of string for Aunt Angela. She's so chronic she'd have to go round with a fifty-foot tow-rope full of clove hitches and bow lines before she'd remember everything. (*He sits at the desk, and takes a bundle of envelopes from his pocket, and passes them to his assistant*) You sort the two competitions, Darbi . . . separate the home-made poems from the best handwriting, and I'll use my indecision to pick out the winners. And we'll disqualify anyone who hasn't written COMP in the top left-hand corner.

Darbishire (*flicking through the envelopes*) Comp. Comp. Comp. . . . Yes, they've all got it on . . . oh, wait a sec; here's one that hasn't. (*He peers at it*)

Jennings (*the stern editor*) Bung it in the waste-paper basket. We can't have chaps forgetting simple instructions like that, or they'll grow up as scatter brained as Aunt Angela.

Darbishire That's who this one's addressed to! And, what's more, it's in your writing!

Jennings WHAT?

Darbishire Look for yourself. Miss Angela Birkinshaw as plain as a pikestaff. (*He opens the envelope, and glances at the letter*) Two double-decker jam sponge cakes, not less than approx. nine inches across, please. (*Reproachfully*) You, great, crumbling, addle-pated ruin, Jennings. (*He hands the letter over*) You've forgotten to post it.

Jennings (*staring at the letter in guilty dismay*) Oh, fish-hooks! If that isn't the rottenest bad luck! I must have been carrying it round for days and now it's got mixed up with the competition envelopes. I know I meant to post it because I can remember doing it.

Darbishire Don't be crazy! How could you have posted it, if here it is!

Jennings No, I mean I can remember MEANING to post it. It's just hard cheese that I forgot.

Darbishire It's nothing of the sort. It's chronic absent-mindedness. Of all

12

the prehistoric clodpolls I ever met, you get the medal for beetle-headedness. . . . There you sit calmly wondering whether your aunt's memory has gone to seed, while all the time the letter's still cluttering up your pocket. My father says that people who . . .

Jennings Oh, shut up, Darbi! I may have made a bit of a bish, but you needn't go on tearing strips off about it all night. What we've got to think of now is what on earth we're going to do.

Darbishire (*after a pause*) I don't suppose the village shop would sell double-decker sponge cakes, but if we got permish to go into Dunham-bury, we might get them there.

Jennings And what about money? I've spent all my rhino on another film for the camera. How much have you got left?

Darbishire About one-and-fourpence. It'd pay the fares all right, but there's not much point in going if we can't afford the cakes when we get there.

Jennings We'll think of something. . . . Let's have a look at the comp. entries first. If we're lucky they'll all be so ghastly that we shan't have to give any prizes at all. Wouldn't it be smashing if they were?

Darbishire Well, they're only six anyway. . . . Funny, all poems . . . no handwriting.

Jennings Well, that's a good thing. If no-one's gone in for it, that makes one sponge cake we don't need.

Darbishire Yes, but who makes the other cake that we DO need?

Jennings Let's not worry about that till we've seen whether the poems are mouldy or not. You read them out while I keep my fingers crossed and hope for the worst.

Darbishire This one's pretty ribby for a kick-off. It's Binns Minor's famous effort. . . .

> I am a pirate on the sea,
> And I am most melAncholEE. . . .

Jennings You're most WHAT?

Darbishire It isn't really melAncholEE, but you have to say it like that to make it fit. It's . . . er . . . it's melancholy, I think. Yes, that's what it really is.

Jennings Never mind what it really *is*. What is it *really*?

Darbishire Melancholy? It means sad. Just like us if we can't think of a prize for . . . Well, I'd better get on, hadn't I . . . ?

> The crew are in a gloomy mood
> Through being rather short of food.
> For quite by chance I dropped their suppers
> Through the scuppers. . . .

That's enough of that one. Isn't it ghastly?

Jennings Frantic. We needn't give a prize for that anyway . . .

Darbishire (*picking up the next*) *Cricket* by C. A. Temple . . .

> You have to have a wicket
> Before you can play cricket.
> One day we made sixty-three for nine.
> And the credit was all mine.

> The bowling was fast, but in spite of that
> Not an eyelid did I bat. . . .

Golly isn't it feeble?

Jennings It's worse than that. All that stuff about his eyelids not batting doesn't even make sense . . .

Darbishire I don't think you quite understand. It's what they call odi-itic— er—idi—omatic, I should say. . . . Here's one by Bromwich Major about a rabbit hutch . . . no good . . . one about the zoo . . .

Jennings Who by?

Darbishire Atkinson . . . useless. . . . And one by Thompson . . . absolute nonsense . . . (*He drops the last one in the basket*)

Jennings That only leaves one more. . . . Gosh, I hope it's mouldy . . .

Darbishire This one's by Venables. Listen:

> Break, break, break,
> On thy cold, grey stones, O sea,
> And I would that my tongue could utter
> The thoughts that arise in me.
> O well, for the fisherman's boy,
> That he shouts with his sister at play!
> O well for the sailor lad
> That he sings in his boat on the bay!

Jennings Phew! That's not bad, is it? Who did you say wrote it?

Darbishire Venables.

Jennings He never did.

Darbishire He must have done. That's Venables' writing; I'd know it anywhere. Not a blot on the whole page. Hang on there's a bit more yet. (*Reading*)

> And the stately ships go on
> To their haven under the hill,
> But O for the touch of a vanished hand,
> And the sound of a voice that is still.
> Break, break, break,
> At the foot of thy crags, O sea!
> But the tender grace of a day that is dead
> Will never come back to me.

Jennings H'm. Well, his poem's certainly a lot better than the others. Mind you, I don't suppose Wordsworth and Tennyson and all that lot would think much of it but it's not bad for a chap of twelve.

Darbishire We'll wizard well have to give him the first prize for a super decent effort like that. Unless of course we can find something wrong with it.

Jennings There must be SOMETHING the matter with it. What about the way he keeps on repeating "O well". He says "O well for the fisherman's boy" and "O well for the sailor lad". People wouldn't really say that would they?

Darbishire Perhaps he couldn't think of anything else to put, so he just thought "O well", and let it go at that.

Jennings We can't disqualify it just because of that: somebody'll kick up a hoo-ha if we do. I suppose we'll just have to think of something else for a prize that's all. If only I hadn't forgotten to post that letter! Oh well it can't be helped.

Darbishire (*sharply*) There you are! You just said it!

Jennings Said what?

Darbishire O well. . . . You said people wouldn't really say that.

Jennings Look here, Darbishire, what's the good of my trying to find something wrong if you keep cracking everything up to the skies and saying how marvellous it is.

Darbishire Sorry, Jen. If you think it's rotten, don't give it a prize.

Jennings I DON'T think it's rotten. It's supersonic and I'd give him a sponge cake like a shock, if only I'd got one to give. Let's think what we could dish him out with instead . . .

Darbishire Yes . . . we're bound to think of something . . .

They pace up and down in silence

ANTHONY BUCKERIDGE

JOSH

JIMMY / JOSH

This story is set in Australia in 1935. Josh Plowman is 14 and very much at odds with the other children at Ryan's Creek where he is visiting his Aunt Clara. In this excerpt he is being plagued by an annoying, whining little red-headed horror called Jimmy

Josh has fallen asleep in the sun. He wakes, a little dazed, and after a few moments reaches for the bottle of squash in his bag. Jimmy is beside him, watching, although at first Josh does not realize he is there. Josh starts to drink

Jimmy Is it nice, Josh?

Josh (*the drink dribbles down his chin*) YOU!

Jimmy Hello, Josh.

Josh What are you doing here? Isn't the world big enough?

Jimmy The liquorice strap was nice. I'm thirsty now.

Josh Well, go home to your mother and ask her for a drink.

Jimmy I'd like some lemon, I would.

Josh You won't be getting any.

Jimmy I like lemon, I do.

Josh So do I, Sonny.

Jimmy Is that your lunch?

Josh (*shortly*) Yes.

Jimmy You've left it in the sun for the flies to get at. You've spoilt your lunch, you have. I'll tell your auntie. She'll be cross.

Josh You're a nice little boy, aren't you?

Jimmy I like lemon, I do.

Josh If you like it as much as all that I suppose you'd better have some. (*He hands it across*) Just a share, Sonny . . . no more! . . . Enough!

Jimmy (*belching and sneezing into the bottle*) It's nasty and hot.

Josh You didn't have to drink it. Give it back.

Jimmy (*finishing it*) 'Ta, Josh.

Josh Ta, my foot.

Jimmy You'll be late.

Josh Late for what?

Jimmy For pancakes at Laura's place.

Josh Holy cow. What do you know about that?

Jimmy (*sniffing, starting to inspect a jam jar he has*) Got some tadpoles, I have. The yabbies wouldn't bite.

Josh What do you know about pancakes at Laura's place?

Jimmy She sent me to check up.

Josh Did she? . . . Well, you've checked.

Jimmy You were supposed to be there at twelve o'clock.

16

Josh It's not twelve o'clock yet.

Jimmy Yes it is. It's way past that. But I knew you didn't want to go, so I didn't wake you up.

Josh says nothing, not to a dangerous one like that

I might see Laura this afternoon. I might tell her you said she could jump in the creek.

Josh Don't you dare!

Jimmy I'd like a chocolate frog, I would.

Josh All you'll be getting from me is a thick ear.

Jimmy If I had a penny, I could go to the lolly shop, and I wouldn't have to go to Laura's place.

Josh I haven't got a penny.

Jimmy You could look.

Josh Do you think I'm a millionaire or something?

Jimmy I could tell Laura you said she was ugly.

Josh You wouldn't!

Jimmy I could tell Harry you stood his sister up because she's fat.

Josh (*staring at him, unbelievingly*) You little flea. And yesterday you carried Aunt Clara's books. You sang hymns. You took up the collection. How much did you take out of the plate for yourself?

Jimmy I could tell Harry you said that. Harry's my cousin, he is. Harry lives next door to me he does. I could tell my dad too. My dad's friend is a policeman in Ballarat.

Josh By golly, Sonny, I bet the only policeman your dad knows is the one he meets when he gets locked up. By golly, I'd like to call your bluff.

Jimmy is silent, peering into his jar

All right! You can have my lunch.

Jimmy If I ate your lunch your auntie would get to hear of it, I think.

Josh You horrible little crook, I hope I'm not around when you grow up. I've got a pencil. Will that do?

Jimmy I've got three pencils. I'd rather have a chocolate frog.

Josh If I give you another penny it's the last. The very, very, final last. If you come blackmailing me again, I'll shake you till you rattle. (*He searches for a penny*) I'll be broke. I'll have nothing to spend for the rest of the week. You go home and tell your mother to drown you . . . (*He realizes his money has gone*)

Jimmy I want my penny.

Josh There isn't any penny.

Jimmy I'll tell.

Josh (*exploding*) You do that! You tell who you like. You tell what you like. I couldn't care less. There isn't any penny. There isn't any money. I've lost it! ALL my money! Lost it!

Jimmy I want my penny.

Josh I'll flatten you, Sonny.

Jimmy I want my penny.

Josh I'm warning you . . .

Jimmy You wouldn't touch me. You wouldn't hit me. I'll tell my mummy ... I'll tell my daddy ... (*He starts to back off, looking uncertain*) I'll tell my mummy ... I'll tell my daddy ... *He runs off crying, leaving the jar*

Meanwhile Josh searches frantically for his money

Josh Holy Cow ... where's that money? Where did I drop it? Where?

IVAN SOUTHALL

MINNOW ON THE SAY

ADAM / DAVID

The "Minnow" is a canoe, and David finds it mysteriously bobbing by the landing stage at the bottom of the garden, where the River Say is affected by heavy rains. He meets the owner, a boy of his own age, Adam, and the two become involved in a most unusual treasure hunt. This is a complicated, fascinating story, well worth reading

Adam I'll explain.

David Yes.

Adam We've not promised not to look for the treasure, but we have promised to spend our time going on expeditions in the Minnow, and going over the tree-bridge. I'll explain about the bridge and show it to you in a minute. Well, we promised to do those two things because, I hope, they'll be the very things that'll help us to the treasure. That is, if the clue is really in the rhyme, as I believe it is. After all, Sarah Codling wasn't likely to have forgotten anything else she was told, or to have made a silly mistake. Her father trusted her more than he did her mother, and she was a sensible age . . . eleven.

David That's true . . . after all, I'm eleven.

Adam There you are. So let's say, as Sarah said, that the only clue is in the rhyme.

David Yet there just isn't one there.

Adam Unless everyone has missed it so far.

David You mean a code?

Adam You can't make up a code in a hurry, in the middle of the night, with your wife nagging you. No, I was thinking of something different. Punctuation. Commas and so on.

David Commas? I don't remember seeing any commas in the rhyme.

Adam That's just it; there aren't any.

David Well, then . . .

Adam But when you say the verse you have to put the punctuation in, in the way you say it. I mean, you have to pause where you think there should be a comma.

David Well, of course.

Adam It's obvious, but it leads to things much less obvious. For instance the Narrative said that Jonathan Codling taught Sarah not just the words of the rhyme but how to say them—where to breathe and pause. That is, he taught her the punctuation.

David Go on.

Adam But why did he bother, unless the punctuation, the pausing, were unusual?

David Go on.

19

Adam But all that's just the kind of thing that gets easily overlooked; and if Judith Codling were upset and worried and cross . . .

David And stupid . . .

Adam And stupid, it's just the kind of thing she'd overlook. She'd hear the words said by Sarah, but she wouldn't hear the way they were said. And very soon the way they were said would be lost.

David Oh, what was the verse? I can't remember it.

Adam I can. I'll say it with the comma pause where Aunt Dinah puts it, where Judith Codling almost certainly put it, and where Sarah . . . I think . . . almost certainly didn't put it . . . that is, at least until she was bullied and beaten out of her common sense:

"When Philip came to the single rose
    Over the water,
The treasure was taken where no-one knows
    None but my daughter."

David To move the comma . . .

Adam Suppose you put it after the first line instead of after the second.

David "When Philip came to the single rose,
    Over the water
The treasure was taken . . ."

Adam OVER THE WATER THE TREASURE WAS TAKEN . . .

David Was it just a bluff then, his going out to hide it that night? Did he get it overseas somewhere, later? But then he didn't go over the water at all: your aunt said he was going to fetch the Spaniards on land, not on sea.

Adam But the sea isn't the only water. It wasn't the water nearest to Jonathan Codling the night he took the treasure from the house.

David The river! The River Say at the bottom of his garden!

Adam And remember those wet stockings that he came back with, and had to change.

David And, of course, they'd have a boat.

Adam He went out in the boat, secretly, with the treasure—

David —And hid it . . . "over the water"—somewhere on the far bank of the river.

Adam This is the beginning of our treasure seeking.

PHILLIPPA PEARCE

NEW LAMPS FOR OLD

ABN-ASUR / ALI-DHINN

The basic story is from "Aladdin" and is set "in the tide and show of ancient time". This scene takes place on a lonely moonlit hillside where great boulders of rock cast sinister shadows. Abn-Asur, the evil Grand Vizier, tries to out-wit the young boy, Ali-Dhinn

Ali-Dhinn is alone

Ali-Dhinn Twice they spoke of a lamp.

Abn-Asur enters from down L

Abn-Asur (*harshly*) What's that about a lamp?
Ali-Dhinn Ah—just a little song, sir. I'm always making silly rhymes. Listen:
>"Lamp of the night,
>Who set you there on high?
>Kindled your light,
>And backed you with the sky?"

Abn-Asur Very pretty. Let's to business. You're an imaginative sort of lad, and you wouldn't be afraid of a little trifling with magic. I want your help with this soupçon of sorcery—to open up the great treasure-cave that I described to you.
Ali-Dhinn I don't mind magic, if it's as easy as you say, sir.

Abn-Asur goes to the rocks, C, *and searches among their crannies*

Abn-Asur There should be star-dust here. It can't have blown away. Not *all*! Ah! A few grains only, but enough for my purposes.

He collects some dust, and comes down to Ali-Dhinn

Now, don't be afraid. I've done this before, and everything will be under control.
Ali-Dhinn That will be a change.
Abn-Asur Star-dust, drifted without sound
>From a dead world far away,
>When you touch again the ground,
>My commands obey.

He scatters the dust in a wide circle about himself and Ali-Dhinn

>Let no demon rouse in wrath;
>Let no danger near;
>Star-dust, guard from fear and death;
>Guard from death and fear.

21

Ali-Dhinn He forgot that bit!

Abn-Asur (*not hearing this*) Hear me, let the magic start:
> Your great power unlock:—
> Strike the solid stone apart—
> Open up the rock!

There is a grinding noise, that swells to the sound of thunder. At the back, the rocks quiver. Slowly they part, to show the jagged mouth of a cave. From inside comes a sparkle of lights. The thunder dies away in silence

There lies the path to fortune, Ali-Dhinn. Take it.

Ali-Dhinn After you, sir.

Abn-Asur No, no! I can't! It's—a tiresome regulation. But you can go in. That's why you're here. Because of my wish to help you—you and your poor, dear, over-worked mother.

Ali-Dhinn There—there might be demons—

Abn-Asur If any was about, he'd be here now! I made this circle, just in case.

Ali-Dhinn You leave it first.

Abn-Asur glares at him, but steps gingerly out of the circle of dust. The wind rises, and he leaps back into it. The wind fades, and Abn-Asur summons his courage, and goes to the rocky cave-mouth. Ali-Dhinn follows him

What light shines from the cave?

Abn-Asur The glitter of a million million jewels, shining in their own beauty. King Suleiman never saw a treasure like this one, in his palmiest days! And there for the taking. *Your* taking.

Ali-Dhinn Somehow it seems too easy.

Abn-Asur The easier the better, surely? Listen, my boy. At first you'll be dazzled by the blaze of jewels. Then you'll see great coffers filled with gold—but touch them not, or you'll be turned to stone. You'll see a blossoming garden, trees heavy with bright fruit, and birds in the branches singing. Look closer. You'll find that each fruit is fashioned from one huge jewel, each bird a silver toy. Touch them not.

Ali-Dhinn Can't I touch anything?

Abn-Asur In a small alcove hangs an unlit lamp. That *only* you may touch. Take it from its hook, and bring it back to me.

Ali-Dhinn A—lamp . . . ?

Abn-Asur When it is safely in my hands, all the rest is yours—the cave and its treasures. I want only that Lamp.

Ali-Dhinn Is it so precious?

Abn-Asur (*hastily*) No, no! Worthless! A lump of dull metal—probably rusty by now.

Ali-Dhinn Why should you want it, then?

Abn-Asur For sentimental reasons! Have you no heart! No gratitude? I saved your life, remember. And your dear mother's! Will you now refuse to give me this small return?

Ali-Dhinn Oh, well . . .

He goes to the cave-mouth, and looks inside. Then covers his eyes

Ah, it's too bright! It hurts my eyes!

Abn-Asur You'll get used to the dazzle. Go! For the treasure! For your
dear mother's sake! For my sake!

*Slowly Ali-Dhinn enters the cave. Abn-Asur runs down and jumps into the
ring of star-dust. He raises his arms and waves them in the air*

> Close the rock, without mishap;
> Leaving just a little gap!

*The wind howls. Thunder sounds. The cave-mouth closes. One small jagged
crack is left, through which the light streams. The wind and thunder fade*

Ali-Dhinn (*from inside the cave*) Hi! Let me out!

Abn-Asur Not until you bring me the Lamp.

Ali-Dhinn Oh, I will! I will!

Abn-Asur peers through the crack, and chuckles

Abn-Asur There he goes! Stumbling down, deep into the cavern. Dazzled
by jewel-light, and weak with terror. Poor, simple soul! He'll fetch the
Lamp, all right. And then . . .? Oh, come on, boy! Hurry! And then—
he thinks I'll let him out. Once I have the Lamp, I'll seal the cave
forever. He'll make no more poems about the moon and the sky. For
never again will he see the moon and sky.

NICHOLAS STUART GRAY

THE PRINCE AND THE PAUPER

EDWARD / TOM

Two boys, Edward Tudor, Prince of Wales, son of Henry VIII and Tom Canty, a boy from a poor London family, were borne on the same day. Young Tom often dreamed and read of the princely life but little did he think he would one day meet the Prince. The scene takes place in an apartment in Westminster just after Edward has punished the soldiers for ill-treating the beggar boy. He has given him food and now they sit together, and talk . . .

(Ideally, the two actors for this duologue should look alike)

Edward What is thy name, lad?

Tom (*eating hungrily*) Tom Canty, an' it please thee, sir.

Edward 'Tis an odd one. Where dost live?

Tom In the city, please thee, sir. Offal Court, out of Pudding Lane.

Edward Offal Court! Truly, 'tis another odd one. Hast parents?

Tom Parents have I, sir, and a granddam likewise that is but indifferently precious to me, God forgive me if it be offence to say it—also twin sisters, Nan and Bet.

Edward Then is thy granddam not overkind to thee, I take it?

Tom Neither to any other is she, so please your worship. She hath a wicked heart, and worketh evil all her days.

Edward Doth she ill treat thee?

Tom There be times that she stayeth her hand being asleep or overcome with drink; but when she hath her judgement clear again, she maketh it up to me with goodly beatings.

Edward (*a fierce look in his eyes*) What! Beatings?

Tom Oh, indeed, yes, please you, sir.

Edward BEATINGS! And thou so frail and little. Hark ye: Before the night comes she shall hie her to the Tower. The King my father . . .

Tom In sooth, you forget, sir, her low degree. The Tower is for the great alone.

Edward True, indeed. I had not thought of that. I will consider of her punishment. Is thy father kind to thee?

Tom Not more than Gammer Canty, sir.

Edward Fathers be alike, mayhap. Mine hath not a doll's temper. He smiteth with a heavy hand, yet spareth me: he spareth me not always with his tongue, though, sooth to say. How doth thy mother use thee?

Tom She is good, sir, and giveth me neither sorrow nor pain of any sort. And Nan and Bet are like to her in this.

Edward How old be these?

Tom Fifteen, an' it please you, sir.

Edward The Lady Elizabeth, my sister, is fourteen, and the Lady Jane Grey, my cousin, is of mine own age, and comely and gracious withal;

24

but my sister, the Lady Mary, with her gloomy mien and—Look you: do thy sisters forbid their servants to smile, lest the sin destroy their souls?

Tom They? Oh, dost think, sir, that THEY have servants?

Edward (*gravely*) And prithee, why not? Who helpeth them undress at night? Who attireth them when they rise?

Tom None, sir. Wouldst have them take off their garments and sleep without—like the beasts?

Edward Their garment? Have they but one?

Tom Ah, good your worship, what would they do with more? Truly, they have not two bodies each.

Edward It is a quaint and marvellous thought! Thy pardon, I had not meant to laugh. But thy good Nan and thy Bet shall have raiment and lackeys enow, and that soon, too: my cofferer shall look to it. No, thank me not; 'tis nothing. Thou speakest well; thou hast an easy grace in it. Art learned?

Tom I know not if I am or not, sir. The good priest that is called Father Andrew taught me, of his kindness, from his books.

Edward Knowst thou the Latin?

Tom But scantly, sir, I doubt.

Edward Learn it lad: 'tis only hard at first. The Greek is harder, but neither these nor any tongues else, I think, are hard to the Lady Elizabeth and my cousin. Thou shouldst hear those damsels at it! But tell me of thy Offal Court. Hast thou a pleasant life there?

Tom In truth, yes, so please you sir, save when one is hungry. There be Punch and Judy shows, and monkeys—oh, such antic creatures! and so bravely dressed!—and there be plays wherein they that play do shout and fight till all are slain, and 'tis so fine to see, and costeth but a farthing—albeit 'tis main hard to get the farthing, please your worship.

Edward Tell me more.

Tom We lads of Offal Court do strive against each other with the cudgel, like to the fashion of the prentices, some times.

Edward (*with enthusiasm*) Marry, that would I not mislike. Tell me more.

Tom We strive in races, sir, to see who of us shall be fleetest.

Edward That would I like also. Speak on.

Tom In summer, sir, we wade and swim in the canals and in the river, and each doth duck his neighbour, and spatter him with water and dive and shout and tumble and—

Edward 'Twould be worth my father's kingdom but to enjoy it once! Prithee go on!

Tom We dance and sing about the Maypole in Cheapside; we play in the sand, each covering his neighbour up; and times we make mud pastry—oh, the lovely mud, it hath not its like for delightfulness in all the world!—we do fairly wallow in the mud, sir—saving your worship's presence.

Edward Oh, prithee, say no more, 'tis glorious! If that I could but clothe me in raiment like to thine, and strip my feet, and revel in the mud once, just once, with none to rebuke me or forbid, meseemeth I could forego the crown!

Tom And if that I could clothe me once, sweet sir, as thou art clad—just once—

Edward Oho, wouldst like it? Then so shall it be. Doff thy rags, and don these splendours, lad! It is a brief happiness but will be not less keen for that. We will have it while we may, and change again before any come to molest.

They quickly change garments. (It will be simpler to use a rich looking cloak and a torn old shirt, unless you have time to dress completely) The two stand before a mirror. They turn and look at each other, then back to the glass again

What dost thou make of this?

Tom Ah, good your worship, require me not to answer. It is not meet that one of my degree should utter the thing.

Edward Then will I utter it. Thou hast the same hair, the same eyes, the same form and stature, the same face and countenance that I bear. Fared we forth naked, there is none could say which was you, and which the Prince of Wales. And, now that I am clothed as thou wert clothed, it seemeth I should be able the more nearly to feel as thou didst when the brute soldier . . . Hark ye, is not this a bruise upon your hand?

Tom Yes, but it is a slight thing, and your worship knoweth that the poor man-at-arms . . .

Edward Peace! It was a shameful thing and cruel! If the king knew . . . (*An idea strikes him*) Stir not a step till I come again! It is a command!

Dressed in his rags he exits through the door, taking with him a document from the table

(*Off*) Unbar the gates!

There are noises and shouts

(*Off*) I am the Prince of Wales, my person is sacred and thou shalt hang for laying thy hand upon me . . .

Left alone, Tom looks in the glass again. Outside, Edward is shouting as he tries to convince someone that he is the Prince of Wales

                                                                    MARK TWAIN

THE PRINCESS AND THE SWINEHERD

AGRAMOR / ETIENNE

Etienne, the spoilt, affected, foppish younger son of King Agramor is playing chess with himself. He makes a move, then crosses to the other side of the table. He sits, moves a man, changes his mind, moves another, just as his father enters

Agramor Cheating yourself, eh? I saw you. Where's your brother?

Etienne I neither know nor care, sir.

Agramor Etienne! I'll have none of your impertinence tonight, my boy. I'm not in the mood to endure it.

Etienne Gout?

Agramor Indigestion. And mind your confounded business, sir! *And* don't dare to raise your eyebrows at me! Whether you like it or not, I happen to be King of this dratted country, *and* your father, and I will have respect!

Etienne Did I move red last? Or white?

Agramor I'll move them for you! All of them!

He picks up the chess-board, and pours the men over Etienne

Now comb those out of your ringlets, hang you!

Etienne I told you at supper that you were over-eating, Father. Too like a horse! And the embers of your temper cannot afford to have the bellows of indigestion blown near them.

Agramor (*gratingly*) If you were five years younger, my son . . . just five! Do you know what I'd do to you, here and now? And really enjoy doing? Can you guess?

Etienne You've been saying just those words, sir, for over fifteen years. And before that, you used to say "if only you were five years older". You're so tender-hearted, Father.

Agramor And you've presumed on that for far too long. Your luck's too good to last! Preposterous puppy! Where's the port?

Etienne Is that altogether wise, sir? Port is very devastating to the temper.

Agramor It can't possibly have a worse effect than you do! (*He pours some port, and drinks*) And it's much more agreeable! I wonder if many men find their sons so vexatious?

Etienne Has Dominic annoyed you, sir?

Agramor What with the pair of you, annoyance is too mild a term. You with your mind in your mirror! Dominic and his magic roses! I've a message for him from the Emperor's daughter that would make his hair curl like yours, if he didn't wear it as though hacked with a sickle!

Etienne So the Emperor's daughter will not favour him. Fancy thinking that she would.

27

Agramor He's out of his mind.

Etienne A displacement quite permanent with him.

Agramor Hold your spiteful tongue, Etienne! Dominic is a fine fellow, and handsome. He could make a good King some day, and make a woman very happy . . . if only he would learn responsibility, and stop behaving like a . . . like a . . .

Etienne Ploughboy? Blacksmith? Swincherd?

Agramor If only he would behave like a Prince.

Etienne You aim too high, my dear Father. You attempt the creation of a silk purse from the ear of a pig.

Agramor I'll box yours in just one minute, young man! I'm going to make your brother into a suitable Prince, if it kills him! I tell you, if he doesn't pull himself together very soon, and act more seemly, I shall . . . I shall . . .

Etienne What will you do, Father?

Agramor I'll . . . yes, I'll disown him! There!

Etienne (*interested at last*) You mean . . . disinherit him?

Agramor Well . . . yes! I'll disinherit him.

Etienne It seems an excellent idea.

He muses over the chess-board, while Agramor paces about

Agramor Now I mustn't lose my temper and speak hastily. I'm not myself this evening. I knew that last capon was over-cooked. Never mind what I've said about Dominic. He's a good boy.

Etienne Father . . .

Agramor What is it?

Etienne You've given him so many chances to mend his ways. Now you wish him to marry . . .

Agramor I thought a lady might bring him to heel.

Etienne And his answer is merely to mock you.

Agramor What do you mean, mock me?

Etienne He will not marry to please you, sir. He makes fun of your wishes by suggesting a courtship of the great Princess. Insulting her in addition, by the sending of a slighting gift.

Agramor The red rose.

Etienne I ask you! A red rose!

Agramor *The* red rose. Stick to facts.

Etienne What matter which red rose? It has offended the lady, and naturally. Sir, be warned! Dominic will add to his brainless conduct the guilt of bringing down on your country the vengeance of the Emperor.

Agramor (*amused*) Hm! You think that, do you?

Etienne Dominic has no thought for such affairs of state. He is not fit to be a Prince.

Agramor What do you advise, Etienne?

Etienne He has asked for the Emperor's daughter . . . simply to mock you, sir. Make him win her . . . or be disinherited.

Agramor Make him . . .? You know, that's quite an idea. *Make* him . . . yes. Thank you, my dear boy, you've been a great help to me. I was wondering what to do next, for the best. Thank you very much.

He pats Etienne lovingly on the shoulder, and his son is rather taken aback

Etienne Not at all. Too overwhelming. All that's needed is a little diplomacy, and . . . (*He snaps his fingers*)
Agramor And Bob's your Uncle! (*He snaps his*)
Etienne Really!
Agramor Where is Dominic? I must get on with this, while the idea is still young and energetic.

He goes to the window and leans out

I wonder if he's out there? Arrh! There's a candle in the woodshed! Burn the whole castle down one dark night! Dominic!
Etienne (*starting*) Father, don't!
Agramor (*hanging from the window*) Dominic. Hey! Hoy!
Etienne Let me send a servant, sir. Pray consider your position. (*He shudders*) Your position!
Agramor *Dominic.*

NICHOLAS STUART GRAY

THE RAGGED SCHOOL

ALFIE / CRIPPLE

In Victorian London many young boys were destitute and hungry, out at nights and in all weathers. Dr Barnado helped many of them and in this play is led to a rooftop area where a group of boys huddle around a chimney for warmth. One is a crippled boy. Suddenly the silence is broken by a terrible scream as a ragged boy, Alfie, climbs over the wall, shivering with cold and fear

Alfie (*calling back down over the wall he has just climbed*) Jacko . . . you all right . . . Jacko . . . Jacko (*To himself*) What's 'appened to 'im. (*Louder*) Jacko!

The crippled lad awakens. He grabs his crutch and moves quickly to Alfie, grabbing him roughly

Cripple Keep yer trap shut . . . I'll break your neck . . . keep yer voice down.
Alfie (*fearfully*) It's Jacko, Cripple . . . 'e fell . . . 'e was climbin' the wall.
Cripple Shut up when I tell yer. (*Pointing to the fanlight*) Look what you done, you woke old Moses, 'e don't like that.

He moves swiftly over to the fanlight and peers cautiously in below

Cripple S'alright, 'e ain't 'eard. Lucky fer you. (*Interested in what he sees*) Sortin' out a new bundle of rags, wonder 'ow much 'e'll get fer that lot.
Alfie (*over the wall*) Jacko . . . you down there?

Cripple moves quickly back to Alfie

Cripple Did you hear what I said?
Alfie What we gonna do?
Cripple 'Oo is 'e anyway? Nobody called Jacko on our lays.
Alfie I met 'im round the bakers dustbins . . .
Cripple (*interrupting*) D'yer get anything?
Alfie No . . . he sleeps down the ware'ouse. I told 'im the rozzers was on the prowl tonight. 'E didn't 'ave nowhere to sleep.
Cripple What d'yer bring 'im 'ere for, there's too many of us up 'ere now. Old Moses finds out we're gonna be in trouble.
Alfie What we gonna do?
Cripple Old Moses don't like trouble with the coppers.
Alfie He fell . . . 'e's layin' down there.
Cripple Get any more up 'ere the roof'll go in.
Alfie 'E might be dead.
Cripple (*suddenly realizing*) 'E better not be. Them coppers find anuvver one of us 'as snuffed it . . . they'll put the net out like we was fishes.
Alfie I'd sooner snuff it than go in the Poor'ouse.

30

Cripple They find 'im layin' down there it'll be our lot. We gotta get 'im up 'ere.

Alfie 'Ow we gonna do that if 'e's spark out?

Cripple I don't care if 'e's kicked the bucket. We gotta get 'im up 'ere before the rozzers find 'im. They're roamin' around like ghosts tonight.

Alfie Who was it they found dead last night?

Cripple Young Nasty's bruvver . . . down by the arches. Now you go back down there . . .

Alfie I ain't goin' back down there again . . .

Cripple You'll do as yer told.

Alfie Supposin' a rozzer comes along.

Cripple You go down there and if your mate's still there . . .

Alfie . . . 'e ain't no mate of mine . . .

Cripple You go round and climb into Old Moses' yard.

Alfie What about his dog?

Cripple You go in that shed where 'e keeps 'is horse. There's a big coil of rope 'angin' on the wall. You give me the whistle when you get back.

Alfie I'm frightened Cripple . . . make one of the others go.

Cripple You goin' or do I 'ave to shove you over?

Alfie fearfully begins to mount the wall. Cripple grabs him

Cripple Remember any sign of coppers, you give us the sign and then scarper.

Alfie Supposin' they catch me?

Cripple Then keep yer gob shut, that's all. Now go on.

BILL OWEN

THE STOWAWAY

AMOS / BOY

The time is 1591. The Boy, Jeremy, is an ordinary small boy who has run away to sea in search of adventure. Amos, an elderly, kind seaman, finds him and hides him

Amos fetches two hunks of bread and arranges them on the table. He goes off for something else. The lid of the basket is raised and the Boy pops out, takes a piece of bread and hides again. Amos returns, notices the bread is missing, looks puzzled, then puts down another piece of bread. He exits. The Boy pops out and takes the second piece of bread. Amos returns with pewter, salt and pepper. He registers surprise at the second missing piece, then fright

He looks round cautiously, draws his sword and goes to the door as if to call help. Then an idea strikes him. He sprinkles pepper all round the room, holding his own nose with one hand. He sprinkles well round the basket. Then he withdraws and waits. He has just turned his back on the basket when there is a tremendous sneeze which startles him

Amos Ha! From all hobgoblins and things that go pop in the night, St Anthony protect me. Come out, whoever you be, and have a care—I am armed! Come you out, I say!

The lid of the basket is raised and a sneezing boy emerges. He punctuates his conversation with sneezes for a bit

Boy Oh, sir, don't kill me, an' it please you, sir.
Amos And why shouldn't I kill you, eh? Trespassing on our ship, lurking in the captain's cabin. . . . It's my plain duty to kill you.

The Boy sneezes hard

(*Offering a large red hankie*) Here, take this.

Boy (*taking it*) Thank you, sir.
Amos (*leaning on his sword surveying the boy*) And would it be you that's been taking chickens' legs, cheeses, meat-pies, and I know not what else from off the Captain's table these ten days past, eh?

The Boy sneezes and nods

Then tell me, prithee, how many of you are there?
Boy (*modestly*) Just me, sir—Jeremy, sir.
Amos Just *you*. No more?
Boy I'm afraid not, sir.
Amos Well enough vittals has gone to feed a regiment of unwanted boys!

Boy Please, sir, I'm a hungry sort of boy. And (*With a glint of spirit*) I'm *not* an unwanted boy, sir. If only the captain knew about me!

Amos (*with meaning*) Ah, if only the captain knew about you! (*He looks nervously over his shoulder at the door*)

Boy The captain'd be glad to have me, sir. I'm a boy of spirit. I want to climb the mast in a howling gale and . . . and . . . and save the captain's life, and fight the Spaniards, sir, and . . . (*He sneezes a lot*)

Amos Ho, indeed! A right valiant boy! And might I ask why you have kept yourself withdrawn from us these ten days since we sailed from Bristol town, eh?

Boy Well, sir, I did mean to confront the captain as soon as we were safe at sea, but—me being a trifle sea-sick, sir, and the captain having so loud a voice and using so many oaths, sir—I stayed in my clothes-basket. I walked the deck at night, sir, and made friends with the ship's cat. He let me share his bowl of water, sir.

Amos Ho, I see. And might I ask who was the great stupid idiot who let you get aboard?

Boy Please, sir, I'd rather not say.

Amos Out with his name. I'll have the captain after him, the great lubber!

Boy Well, please, sir, it was you. I was hiding in the captain's clothes-basket, and you carried it on board and put it there.

Amos Oh . . . h'm. . . . And now what are we to do with you, eh?

Boy Anything you like, sir. You'll find me very brave, sir, and strong, and a loyal sort of boy, sir. I'm a . . .

Amos Yes, I know that, you've been over all that. What made you run away from home, eh?

Boy Well, sir, I've got an aunt.

Amos Nothing to boast about in that. Most boys have aunts. Even *I* once had an aunt!

Boy Yes, sir, but my aunt was a bit *sour*, sir. She used to have a birch, sir, and very strong wrists. But I expect I deserved it. But, you see, I got tired of it, and I've always wanted to sail the seas in a great ship, sir, and be a sailor, and climb the rigging, and fight Spaniards, and wear earrings, sir, like you do, and—and play the pipe, sir—like you play it!

Amos D'you like the way I play the pipe, eh?

Boy Oh, I think it's beautiful, sir. It makes me cry, it's so lovely.

Amos Come, you're a very intelligent boy, a most intelligent boy. Yes, I'll help you; you can rely on old Amos. Shake hands, boy.

Boy Jeremy, sir.

They shake hands solemnly

Amos Jeremy, then we're ship-mates. Now, what to do next about you? *H'm*, I fear—I fear the captain must be told.

Boy (*wincing*) Oh . . . he's such a ferocious man, sir.

Amos Oh, he is; but don't you fear, *I* can handle him. Ha, there's only one person that's not afeared of the captain and that's *me*—

Captain (*off*) Amos! Amos!

Amos (*jumping nearly out of his skin*) Oh ... quick, here he is. Hide, quickly ... (*Aloud, answering the Captain*) Sir!

He pulls the clothes-basket out towards Jeremy, and Jeremy jumps in. Amos covers him up, then turns and busies himself at the table, humming to himself

DAVID SCOTT DANIELL

THE THWARTING OF BARON BOLLIGREW

BOLLIGREW / BLACKHEART

Baron Bolligrew of the Bolligrew Islands tyrannizes the peasants, pulls down churches, and hunts all sorts of animals and birds. Oblong has been sent by the Duke to subdue Bolligrew, and here Bolligrew is persuading huge, stupid Blackheart to challenge Oblong to a duel

Blackheart is mindlessly gazing over the audience, sucking one end of his moustache as Bolligrew approaches him

Bolligrew Blackheart. (*He hands him a cigar*) Have a cigar.

Blackheart Mm? Oh, thanks. (*He takes it*)

Bolligrew (*lighting his cigar*) We shall have trouble with that fellow, Blackheart.

Blackheart Little fat feller just now?

Bolligrew That's the one. He, er . . . ₁ (*He takes Blackheart by the elbow; they patrol downstage, smoking cigars*) He, er—he fancies himself as a bit of a fighter for one thing.

Blackheart (*interested*) Oh?

Bolligrew Mm. Didn't you notice how he kept lookin' at you?

Blackheart No?

Bolligrew Oh.

Blackheart (*anxiously*) How was he lookin' at me?

Bolligrew Well, you know, like he thought you were a big bag of wind.

Blackheart What?

Bolligrew Mm, you know, like he thought you were a big feller but not much good in a scrap.

Blackheart He didn't!

Bolligrew He did. I wondered how you could put up with it. "How does Blackheart put up with it?" That's what I kept wonderin'. I mean, it's not the thing, is it, for a gentleman to put up with that?

Blackheart (*going*) I'll flatten 'im!

Bolligrew Er . . . Blackheart.

Blackheart turns. Bolligrew beckons him back

There IS a complication.

Blackheart Oh?

Bolligrew Mm. This feller's a Royal Knight Errant, ye see. Got the purple mantle.

Blackheart I'm not afraid of . . .

Bolligrew No, no, no . . . of course you're not. But we could have trouble from the mainland you see. I mean, we don't want a Royal Commission, do we? I mean we don't want the Islands SWARMING with Knights Errant, poking their long noses into every blazing thing, do we?

Blackheart (*sobered*) Goo' Lord no. Better leave 'im alone, eh?

Bolligrew Mmm—don't know about that. You ARE a gentleman.

Blackheart (*laughing*) Well, I should 'ope so!

Bolligrew Yes. Well then, you're entitled to satisfaction. But, just make sure you do it in the proper form.

Blackheart Right. (*He glances off uneasily, then draws close to Bolligrew*) What IS the proper form?

Bolligrew Oh. Well. First, you must throw down the gauntlet.

Blackheart (*gazing at it*) Me gauntlet.

Bolligrew That's it. Chuck it down. That's a challenge. Then if he picks it up . . .

Blackheart Yes?

Bolligrew You can clobber him.

Blackheart Right.

Bolligrew If he DON'T pick it up . . .

Blackheart Yes?

Bolligrew Then insult him. And if he STILL won't fight . . .

Blackheart Yes?

Bolligrew Then you can't touch him.

Blackheart Well what's the good of that?

Bolligrew Ah. You see, old man, you must do it in front of witnesses. This feller, ye see, has set himself up as the Champion of the poor and needy. And if 'e won't fight after that . . .

Blackheart Yes?

Bolligrew Well, then, his sweaty friends will see what sort of Champion they've got won't they?

Blackheart (*with a grunt*) Yes, but look 'ere, where's me satisfaction?

Bolligrew That, Blackheart, would satisfy any gentleman that ever breathed.

Blackheart Oh. Right. Let's have it again. That's gauntlet, insult, sweaty . . .?

Bolligrew (*looking at him dubiously*) Tell you what. Come up to the castle and I'll jot it down for you.

Blackheart Oh. Right.

ROBERT BOLT

ZIGGER ZAGGER

HARRY / RECRUITING SERGEANT

Written specially for the National Youth Theatre in 1967 the play looks at the life of Harry Philton, a football fan with a poor school record and not much of a future. His teacher comments "You're a nation of watchers, not doers". This scene shows him at the recruiting office. The songs could be cut and the actor playing the Recruiting Officer might double the Medical Officer (quick change into a white coat and spectacles). It makes a neat finish

Harry I want to join the armed forces.

Recruiting Sergeant What makes you want to do that then, son?

Harry I feel like it Fight for me country.

Recruiting Sergeant Do you stand up at the pictures when they play *God Save the Queen*?

Harry Yes.

Recruiting Sergeant What do you want to go in?

Harry The army.

Recruiting Sergeant Well, I'm not exactly in the Girl Guides. What branch? What branch, son? The army is like a tree. Digs in its roots, sprouts forth, brings on sap, spreads out its leaves, drains the soil where it stands, provides shade from the sun; it has branches, bark and bite. What branch?

Harry Fighting branch.

Recruiting Sergeant Fighting, eh? Yes, you look a fighting man, you do. Put your fists up. Yes. Bit old-fashioned, but there, you've got the basics. Why don't you learn a trade?

Harry No, I could do that out here. I want to fight.

Recruiting Sergeant But when you're finished? When your time's up?

Harry I'm not looking to the time when my time's up. I'll have either got somewhere, or I'll have found a soldier's grave.

Recruiting Sergeant I see. Been watching *The Three Musketeers*, have you?

Harry No, I haven't.

Recruiting Sergeant We always get a rush of recruits after *The Three Musketeers*. It was *Z Cars* which finished us up though. They all went into the police force, the six-footers did. The Coldstream Guards were badly run down. Had to lower their height limit. And *The Navy Lark* didn't help. Still, there's something about a soldier.

(*Singing*) There's something about a soldier,
There's something about a soldier,
There's something about a soldier
That is fine, fine, fine.
He may be a sergeant-major,
He may be a common lance jack,

He may be a dirty private,
But he's fine, fine, fine.
(*Speaking*) Is this your idea of the infantry?
It's time you got up to date
Like the army.
If your idea of the infantryman is only
A muddy footslogger with a rifle
It's time you got up to date.
(*Singing*) There's something about a soldier,
What is it about a soldier?
Is it his ribbons or his bearing
That is fine, fine, fine?
No, it's his technological training,
His nuclear warfare tactics,
His germinology strategy
That is fine, fine, fine.
(*Speaking*) Our men ride into battle
In armoured vehicles.
They are equipped with the latest radio.
Their anti-tank weapons include guided missiles.
As well as improved recoilless guns
And rocket launchers.
There is a new mortar,
The eighty-one millimetre,
With greatly increased range and accuracy;
A new general purpose machine-gun
To replace the old Vickers and Bren.
(*Singing*) There's something about a soldier,
There's something about his training,
There's something about his background
That is fine, fine, fine.

He used to be from Glasgow Gorbals,
From Tyneside or the East End,
But now he's up from Cambridge
And he's fine, fine, fine.

With his military air
You should see the girls all stare,
There's something about a soldier
That is fine, fine, fine.
(*Speaking*) Even the rifles are new—
Self-loading, high velocity weapons.
A single platoon could take on more heavy tanks
Than a whole battalion in World War Two.
Do you want to join?
Do you want to be a man?
Harry Have you still got room for the fighting man? Like meself?

Recruiting Sergeant 'Course we have. Muscles like yours still has the power to turn the wogs into custard. What school did you go to?
Harry Millwall Comprehensive.
Recruiting Sergeant Did they have a C.C.F. there, son?
Harry They had everything there. Free films, sex talks, speech training, the lot.
Recruiting Sergeant Did they have C.C.F.?
Harry If they did, I never got it. What is it?
Recruiting Sergeant Combined Cadet Force.
Harry Nah. We didn't have that.
Recruiting Sergeant Then you can't be Officer Cadet material. But then neither was I. Failed on accent. Like to be like me, would you?
Harry You're a fighting man. I want to be like you.
Recruiting Sergeant Take off your shirt then, wait for the medical.

Harry takes off his shirt

Harry (*singing*) There was something about the soldier,
               The old-fashioned style soldier,
               The old bayonet-thrusting soldier,
               That was fine, fine, fine.

               He slogged his way to a foreign coffin,
               Never a care for noffin',
               Now he's replaced by a bloody boffin,
               It's just fine, fine, fine.

               With his scientific lore
               He kills millions more than ever before.
               There's something about a soldier
               That is fine, fine, fine.

The scene can end here if the Recruiting Sergeant is not doubling the Medical Officer

   The Recruiting Sergeant exits. The Medical Officer enters

Medical Officer Right, to the medical. Jump up and down on that chair. Deep breath in, deep breath out, read that with this over your right eye, now the left eye, take this bottle round there, fill it. Right bend your knees. Stretch. Good. See if you can hear what I'm saying. (*Whispering*) Can you hear this?
Harry (*whispering*) Yes.
Medical Officer All right. Up on that chair. Again, yes, drop your trousers. I see. Not fit. Grade C.
Harry Not fit?
Medical Officer Not fit. A mass of minor ailments from dandruff to athlete's foot. You're even pigeon-toed. You might squeeze in in a major war, but not on the local stuff. We don't want you. You're not A-one. You're not A-one.
Chorus (*singing*) Oh put the ref into hospital
               Where they will treat him so kind,

'Cos we can't have a ref on this ground
Who is both lame, deaf and blind.
A-one, we must have men who are A-one, A-one,
A-one, A-one, we must have men who are A-one, A-one.

PETER TERSON

AND I DANCE MINE OWN CHILD

GRANDMOTHER / GRISELDA

It is the year 1879. Griselda is 10 and Great Grandmother Curfew is 110. But their roles are reversed. Griselda looks after the old lady as if she were a child. She loves her dearly, and takes her responsibilities (which are considerable) very seriously. The scene takes place in the garden outside the cottage. Great Grandmother Curfew has been eating nuts

Grandmother (*pretending*) Oh them squirrels . . . them squirrels. They've been at the nuts again.
Griselda I'm going to give you a dose, tonight, Grandma.
Grandmother I don't want no dose, Grissie.
Griselda Yes, Gramma, you do.
Grandmother I don't like doses. They're that nasty.
Griselda They're good for you.
Grandmother I won't take no dose, I tell you.
Griselda If you don't you'll wake up in the middle of the night with the collywobbles.
Grandmother No, I won't, Grissie.
Griselda I think you will, Gramma.
Grandmother Why do you think so?
Griselda Well, I just do think so. And I think the squirrels will too, if somebody don't give them doses.
Grandmother (*realizing she has been found out*) No, I won't . . . I won't . . . unless Bella has one too.
Griselda All right, Gramma, and you see how good she is about it. (*She gives medicine to the doll, Bella*) You'll be as good as Bella, I know.
Grandmother No, I won't . . . I won't.
Griselda Come along.
Grandmother Can I have a sweetie after?
Griselda Yes.
Grandmother Two sweeties?
Griselda Yes.
Grandmother And will you tell me a story?
Griselda Yes.
Grandmother And sing me to sleep?
Griselda Yes, Gramma. . . . Come along, now.

Grandmother takes her dose and her sweets. Griselda settles her for the night

Grandmother What tale will you tell me tonight, Grissie?
Griselda I'll tell you the tale about the giant, Gramma.
Grandmother The giant who had three heads?
Griselda Yes, that one.

41

Grandmother And he lived in a brass castle?

Griselda Yes, that one.

Grandmother I like that one. Now, then, you tell it to me, and mind you don't go and leave any of it out.

Griselda Once upon a time there was a Giant and he had THREE HEADS and lived in a BRASS CASTLE.

Grandmother (*with eyes shut*) Have you told me the story, Grissie?

Griselda Yes, Gramma.

Grandmother All of it?

Griselda Every word of it.

Grandmother Didn't you leave a bit out?

Griselda Not one bit.

Grandmother I like that story. Now, you sing me to sleep.

Griselda (*singing*) Hush hush hush . . .
> And I dance mine own child
> And I dance mine own child
> Hush hush hush

Grandmother (*opening her eyes*) Now don't you go and leave me Grissie. I aren't asleep yet.

Griselda repeats the song

Grandmother I aren't asleep yet. Don't go and leave me, Grissie.

Griselda repeats the song. At the end, seeing Grandmother is asleep, she creeps very quietly away

ELEANOR FARJEON

BOYS AND GIRLS COME OUT TO PLAY

BELINDA / WENDY

I took this scene out of a script of one of the TV series "Menace", so it won't be possible to read the whole story. Belinda is the sort of difficult, scheming, ruthless child whom no-one understands. Her night-time exploits eventually have unpleasant consequences . . . remember the legend of London Bridge being built with the remains of people? Well, the final shots in the film of a cement mixer, added to the knowledge that Wendy has disappeared leave one in little doubt . . . In this scene the weaker girl allows herself to be led into trouble. The haunting tune from the musical box (lightly played on a piano, and recorded) helps to create an atmosphere both childlike and uncanny . . . menacing . . .

Belinda has just played Wendy a tune on her musical box

Belinda How do you like it? (*She shuts the box*)
Wendy Fabulous. Can I borrow it? (*She snatches at it*)
Belinda 'Course not. Children don't borrow things like that.
Wendy Oh, what sort of things do children borrow, then?
Belinda Things that don't get broken.
Wendy Oh.
Belinda Do you know the words?
Wendy What words?
Belinda These words, you great nit. (*She plays the tune and sings*)
    Boys and girls, come out to play,
    The moon doth shine as bright as day,
    Leave your supper and leave your sleep
    And join your playfellows in the street . . . (*She shuts the lid*)

There are some more words but they don't matter

Wendy They're a bit soppy.
Belinda What?
Wendy The words. "Join your playfellows in the street . . ." Why don't they just say school friends?
Belinda That's poetry. It's no good if it isn't old fashioned . . . Why don't WE go out and play at night?
Wendy What?
Belinda They must have done it sometime or it wouldn't be in a nursery rhyme, would it? Why don't WE?
Wendy But we'd get into a terrible row.
Belinda IF they catch us . . .
Wendy They will.
Belinda Go when they're asleep . . .
Wendy We'd wake them up going downstairs.

Belinda Go out the window. (*She goes to the window*)

Wendy (*joining her*) How d'you reach the ground?

Belinda I can manage down over the porch, I've done it lots of times before. It's great fun, but you need someone to share.

Wendy I'm at the back.

Belinda You've a ladder.

Wendy I couldn't reach it.

Belinda 'Course you couldn't, stupid. I'll put the ladder up for you.

Wendy But . . . it's silly . . .

Belinda 'Course it's not, don't be soppy . . . it's fun.

Wendy But what would we do? (*She sits at the table*)

Belinda Lots of things. First of all *we* can do it to see if it works . . . then we could get some of the others to come along. Margie would be fun.

Wendy Why don't you do it with her then?

Belinda Because I can boss you.

Wendy But I don't want to, Belinda . . . it's a silly idea.

Belinda Huh . . . you're just scared.

Wendy No, I'm not.

Belinda You are.

Wendy I'm not . . . but we need our sleep.

Belinda "Leave your supper and leave your sleep" it says. They must have done it sometime or they wouldn't have written a rhyme about it.

Wendy No . . . but . . . (*Moving* L)

Belinda Right then. Be ready to-night . . . at two o'clock.

Wendy Two o'clock in the night?

Belinda Well, there wouldn't be much point in two in the afternoon, would there stupid?

Wendy No . . . but . . .

Belinda Come on, you'd better go now, Wendy. Right now. Not a word to anyone.

Wendy BELINDA.

Belinda Do you need to go to the loo?

Wendy No.

Belinda You look as though you do.

Wendy I don't.

Belinda Good-bye . . . and remember what I said.

Wendy goes

There's no end to what you can get up to at night . . . no end to it . . . (*She plays the music*)

JAMES MCTAGGART

THE CHILDREN'S HOUR

MARY / ROSALIE

Mary Tilford is a resentful, difficult girl of about thirteen, a troublemaker. She spreads rumours about the private lives of the two young women principals of her school, causing the place to be closed down. In this scene, another pupil, the rather weak and pathetic Rosalie, has come to stay the night at the Tilford home. Mary is hiding, lying in wait when Rosalie enters

Time: the mid-thirties, America

Mary (*loudly*) Whooooo!

Rosalie jumps

Whooooo!

Rosalie, frightened, makes for the door

(*Laughing*) You're a goose.

Rosalie (*belligerently*) Oh, so it's you. Well, who likes to hear funny noises at night? You could have been a werewolf.

Mary What would a werewolf do with you?

Rosalie Just what he'd do with anybody else. Isn't it funny about school?

Mary What's funny about it?

Rosalie Don't act like you can come home every night.

Mary Maybe I can from now on. Maybe I'm never going back.

Rosalie Am I going back? I don't want to stay home.

Mary What'll you give to know?

Rosalie Nothing. I'll just ask my mother.

Mary Will you give me a free T.L. if I tell you?

Rosalie (*thinking for a moment*) All right. Lois Fisher told Helen that you were very smart.

Mary That's an old one. I won't take it.

Rosalie You got to take it.

Mary Nope.

Rosalie (*laughing*) You don't know anyway.

Mary I know what I heard, and I know Grandma phoned your mother in New York five dollars and eighty-five cents to come and get you right away. You're just going to spend the night here. I wish Evelyn could come instead of you.

Rosalie But what's happened? Peggy and Helen and Evelyn and Lois went home tonight, too. Do you think somebody's got secret measles or something?

Mary No.

Rosalie Do *you* know what it is? How'd you find out? (*No answer*) You're

45

always pretending you know everything. You're just faking. (*She flounces away and sits on the ottoman*) Never mind, don't bother telling me. I think curiosity is very unladylike, anyhow. I have no concern with your silly secrets, none at all. (*She twirls round on the ottoman, stops, and after a long pause*) What did you say?

Mary I didn't say a thing.

Rosalie Oh. (*She twirls around again*)

Mary laughs. She rises, puts the jigsaw puzzle in a drawer of a highboy

Mary But now suppose I told you that I just may have said that you were in on it?

Rosalie (*stopping twirling*) In on what?

Mary The secret. Suppose I told you that I *may have* said that you told me about it?

Rosalie (*rising*) Why, Mary Tilford! You can't do a thing like that. I didn't tell you about anything.

Mary laughs

Did you tell your grandmother such a thing?

Mary Maybe.

Rosalie (*crossing to below R love-seat, turning to Mary*) Well, I'm going right up to your grandmother and tell I didn't tell you anything— whatever it is. You're just trying to get me into trouble, like always, and I'm not going to let you. (*She starts for the arch*)

Mary (*crossing to below the armchair*) Wait a minute, I'll come with you.

Rosalie (*stopping UL of the armchair*) What for?

Mary I want to tell her about Helen Burton's bracelet.

Rosalie (*slowly turning to Mary*) What about it?

Mary Just that you stole it.

Rosalie (*crossing to Mary*) Shut up! I didn't do any such thing.

Mary Yes, you did.

Rosalie (*tearfully*) You made it up. You're always making things up.

Mary You can't call me a liar, Rosalie Wells. That's a kind of dare and I won't take a dare.

She starts for the arch. Rosalie blocks her way

I guess I'll go tell Grandma, anyway. Then she can call the police and they'll come for you and you'll get tried in court.

She slowly backs Rosalie to behind R end of L love-seat. While she speaks, she pulls Rosalie's glasses down on her nose and pulls her hair

And you'll go to one of those prisons, and you'll get older and older, and when you're good and old they'll let you out, but your mother and father will be dead by then and you won't have any place to go and you'll beg on the streets—

Rosalie (*crying*) I didn't steal anything. I borrowed the bracelet and I was going to put it back as soon as I'd worn it to the movies. I never meant to keep it.

Mary Nobody'll believe that, least of all the police. You're just a common, ordinary thief. Stop that bawling. You'll have the whole house down here in a minute.

Rosalie You won't tell? Say you won't tell.

Mary Am I a liar?

Rosalie No.

Mary Then say: "I apologize on my hands and knees".

Rosalie I apologize on my hands and knees. Let's play with the puzzle.

Mary Wait a minute. Say: "From now on, I, Rosalie Wells—(*Crossing her wrists in front of her*)—am the vassal of Mary Tilford and will do and say whatever she tells me under the solemn oath of a knight."

Rosalie (*crossing downstage to below* R *end of love-seat*) I won't say that. That's the worst oath there is.

Mary starts down R

Mary! Please don't—

She quickly follows Mary and stops her below R *love-seat*

Mary Will you swear it?

Rosalie (*sniffing*) But then you could tell me to do anything.

Mary (*starting to move* R) Say it quick or I'll—

Rosalie (*hurriedly*) From now on—(*Slowly turning and crossing* L *to* L *love-seat, holding her wrists crossed in front of her*) I, Rosalie Wells, am the vassal of Mary Tilford and will do and say whatever she tells me under the solemn oath of a knight.

Mary Don't forget that.

                                                              LILLIAN HELLMAN

GOBLIN MARKET

LAURA / LIZZIE

I have adapted this from the long allegorical poem written in 1859. It's about two sisters, one who succumbs to temptation, one who resists. Although here the "temptation" is goblin men and luscious fruits, the poem is a moral tale of "good and evil" so popular with Victorian people

Laura has disobeyed and taken fruit from the goblin men. Now, all alone, she waits for them to come back with more. But they do not come. Her sister, Lizzie, comes to get her

Lizzie Dear, you should not stay so late,
Twilight is not good for maidens;
Should not loiter in the glen
In the haunts of goblin men.
Do you not remember Jeanie,
How she met them in the moonlight,
Took their gifts both choice and many,
Ate their fruits and wore their flowers
Plucked from bowers
Where summer ripens at all hours?
But ever in the noonlight
She pined and pined away;
Sought them by night and day,
Found them no more but dwindled and grew grey;
Then fell with the first snow.
While to this day no grass will grow
Where she lies low:
I planted daisies there a year ago
That never blow.
You should not loiter so.

Laura Nay hush. . . . Nay hush, my sister:
I ate and ate my fill,
Yet my mouth waters still;
And oh, I must buy more . . .
Have done with sorrow,
Lizzie, I'll bring you plums
Fresh on their mother twigs,
Cherries worth getting;
You cannot think what figs
My teeth have met in,
What melons icy cold
Piled on a dish of gold
Too huge for me to hold,

48

What peaches with a velvet nap,
Pellucid grapes without one seed:
Odorous indeed must be the mead
Whereon they grow, and pure the wave they drink
With lilies at the brink
And sugar sweet their sap.

Lizzie The sunset flushes
Those furthest loftiest crags;
Come, Laura, not another maiden lags,
No wilful squirrel wags,
The beasts and birds are fast asleep . . .

Laura The hour is early still,
The dew not fallen, the wind not chill:
I'm listening, but I cannot hear
The customary cry,
"Come buy, come buy".
Not for all my watching
Can I see even one goblin
Racing, whisking, tumbling, hobbling;
Let alone the herds
That used to tramp along the glen,
In groups or single,
Of brisk fruit-merchant men . . .

Lizzie O Laura, come;

(She looks fearfully about her as she hears the goblins calling)

I hear the fruit-call, but I dare not look:
You should not loiter longer at this brook:
Come with me home.
The stars rise, the moon bends her arc,
Each glow-worm winks her spark,
Let us get home before the night grows dark:
For clouds may gather
Though this is Summer weather,
Put out the lights and drench us through;
Then if we lost our way what should we do?

Laura Why should YOU hear that cry alone,
That goblin cry,
"Come buy our fruits, come buy".
Must I then buy no more such dainty fruit?
Must I no more such succous pasture find,
Come deaf and blind . . .

Lizzie Come, Laura, come . . . and do not weep . . .

Laura *(desolate and unhappy)* I feel my heart will break.

CHRISTINA ROSSETTI

THE GOOSE GIRL

AGATHA / GRIZELDA

Agatha is travelling with her step-sister Grizelda, a girl of far sweeter disposition. Encouraged by her mother, she plans to harm Grizelda so that she herself can marry the Prince and become rich. You will need to use your imagination to make the "magic" section work, but it can be done

Scene: the bank of a stream which runs close to a road. The stream must be imagined to be flowing between the players and the audience. If it can be placed in front of the CURTAIN, *so much the better. The only prop required is a log or stone for Grizelda to sit on*

Agatha enters, carrying a light travelling-bag

Agatha Grizelda, are you coming?

Grizelda appears

Grizelda Yes, Agatha, here I am. I was just seeing that Falada was properly looked after.

Agatha Ugh, that horse—he gives me the shudders. How *can* you put up with a horse that talks?

Grizelda He's a beautiful horse, Agatha, and so clever. This is a pleasant spot, Agatha . . . this lovely grass and that cool stream, and all the trees. I'm tired and stiff from riding so far and I'm going to sit down over there. (*She does so*) Oh, Agatha, dear—will you take my little gold goblet and get me a drink from the brook?

Agatha Of course I'll take your goblet—(*She does so—from the travelling-bag*)—and certainly I'll get a drink of water (*She reaches down into the brook—towards the audience—and stands up*) but not for *you*—you milk-faced ninny—for *myself*! (*She drinks in a melodramatic fashion*)

Grizelda Agatha, really—your manners! By all means have a drink, but I think you might have served me first.

Agatha Serve *you*? Never! *Never.* (*Coming closer and peering down at Grizelda*) Don't you realize, you spoiled brat, that I *hate* you?

Grizelda Agatha, what's the matter with you?

Agatha Every day, month hafter month, I've had to stand aside and see you petted and pampered and fawned over and smiled upon, while I'm ignored.

Grizelda Agatha, this is past a joke.

Agatha This is no joke! (*She walks a step nearer, drawing a knife from her girdle*) Do you see what I have here? A pretty little dagger—see how it gleams—see how *sharp* it is—look, *darling* Grizelda!

Grizelda (*quite composed*) And what are you going to do with it?

Agatha (*now in a white-hot temper*) I'm going to *kill* you, Princess Grizelda!

50

*She reaches for Grizelda's wrist as she swings the dagger up to strike. On its
downward path it stops as at an invisible barrier. Her fingers cannot reach
Grizelda's wrist. Savagely she tries again. The same thing happens. Now she
is frightened*

Agatha (*in a frightened whisper*) What's this? I can't touch you—I can't
reach you—there's something around you, like a wall—it's *magic*!

Grizelda (*unmoved*) Yes, dear stepsister. It's magic. Just a square of silk
with three drops of blood on it. (*She draws the kerchief from her neck*)
But it's strong enough for me, and it's *too* strong for you.

Agatha (*crouching back*) Magic! You *witch*! You *witch*! To look so
innocent, and to be so wicked . . .

Grizelda Hard words hurt less than dagger-blows. But, Agatha, why
should you hate me? What have I ever done to you? I've never harmed
you—I've tried to be friends . . .

Agatha (*crying with rage and frustration*) Because you're younger than I
am, and prettier than I am, and you're going to be married to a Prince,
and I'll probably never marry at all now, and—oh!—just because I *hate*
you . . .

Grizelda And I thought you were my friend. We must return at once to my
father. He will know what to do but I *must* have that water. My throat
burns . . .

*She picks up the goblet and dips it into the brook. As she does so, her magic
kerchief is dropped somehow*

*As it falls, the East Wind enters noisily. He swoops and snatches up the
kerchief and dances off with it, waving, to simulate flight of silk on breeze*

Enter West Wind in hot pursuit. Exit East Wind, flourishing kerchief

*Grizelda does not notice all this, as she is drinking, but Agatha does, and as
Grizelda lowers the cup from her lips (or at some other appropriate movement)
Agatha steals up and pounces upon the unlucky Princess. She grasps her wrist
and flashes the dagger*

Agatha Now I've got you, Miss *Magic*.

Grizelda Oh! Oh! My kerchief—why doesn't it stop her? Why doesn't it
protect me? It's *gone*! It's *gone*! Heaven have mercy on me!

Agatha That's it—pray, my pretty one, pray. Yes, your magic has gone, on
the wings of the wind. See—there it flutters, away and out of sight.

Grizelda (*screaming*) Guards, guards, help! Help! I am in danger!

Agatha Scream away—it won't help you a bit. The guards are all in *my*
power. *Now.* (*She raises the dagger*)

Grizelda Agatha, no! Please wait! Oh, Agatha!

Agatha Wait! Perhaps it might be more amusing to let you live—yes—yes!
Milksop, you *shall* live, and you shall wish you were dead!

*She flings Grizelda away from her, confident now, and tucks the dagger away
again*

Grizelda What are you going to do?

Agatha I am going to be Grizelda, and you shall see it happen—*I* shall marry Prince Stefan, and you shall scrub floors—*I* shall be happy, and you shall weep. Oh, this is *beautiful*—a *much* better plan!

Grizelda Oh, no!

Agatha whips out the dagger

Agatha Then you prefer to die?

Grizelda No, Agatha, no! Oh, no!

Agatha You *are* hard to please. But now you shall swear an oath. Raise your hand like this—no, kneel down. Now then, say this after me—I, Princess Grizelda . . .

Grizelda I, Princess Grizelda . . .

Agatha Do swear, on my honour . . .

Grizelda Do swear, on my honour . . .

Agatha And on my mother's soul . . .

Grizelda And on my mother's soul . . .

Agatha That I will never reveal . . .

Grizelda That I will never reveal . . .

Agatha To any living soul . . .

Grizelda To any living soul . . .

Agatha What has happened here to-day . . .

Grizelda What has happened here to-day . . .

Agatha Or *who* or *what* I am . . .

Grizelda Or who or what I am.

Agatha Good! Now I'm safe. You have sworn a sacred oath, both on your own honour and on your dead mother's soul. You *dare* not tell.

Grizelda No, I dare not tell.

Agatha Give me your rings. Now your coronet—we will go behind those ˙bushes and change our clothes. Go—and then I shall ride your wonderful Falada—and you can walk in the dust. Go!

Grizelda goes

And then Falada shall die. He *might* talk. (*She goes*)

A. LINTERN

IN NEED OF CARE

RITA / SHIRLEY

Rita and Shirley have run away from a remand home, and have spent the night in a barn. The scene is set in the barn, early the next morning. Shirley is sharper and more knowing than vulnerable Rita

Shirley Wake up, kid.

There is some movement in the straw. It is Rita, lying on her stomach. She stirs herself slightly and pulls a piece of sacking to herself against the cold. Shirley is now seated on a bale of straw, rummaging about in a large, cheap-looking handbag. She pulls out a crisp pack which contains two or three crisps. She eats these and shakes the remaining crumbs into her mouth. She screws up the empty crisp pack and throws it on to the floor. She rummages again in the handbag, finds nothing of interest, puts it down, and climbs up on the pile of straw to the window, giving Rita a sharp kick as she goes

Rita Ow! (*She moves up into a sitting position, resting on her elbows*)

Shirley goes to the window, rubbing a space in the grime with her elbow to see through

(*Sitting up*) I'm cold.
Shirley Get up, then.
Rita Did you sleep much?
Shirley No.
Rita Nor me. Too cold.
Shirley We'll be all right tonight. You'll see.
Rita (*getting up on to her feet*) I hope so. How far is it?
Shirley Where?
Rita To your auntie's.
Shirley Dunno. Not far.
Rita How far?
Shirley (*irritably*) I don't know. About ten miles.
Rita Can we walk ten miles?
Shirley 'Course we can.

Rita picks up the handbag and searches in it

Rita Let's get going right away.
Shirley What for?
Rita I'm hungry.
Shirley Don't be daft.
Rita Well, I am.
Shirley Walking won't help, it will make you hungrier.
Rita Where's my purse?

Shirley I never took it.
Rita I never said you did.
Shirley You'd better not.
Rita Oh, I remember.

Rita goes over to the straw where she was sleeping and searches. Shirley comes down from the window and goes to the door and looks out

Shirley Some mothers do have 'em.

Rita finds her handkerchief in the straw. It is tied in knots with her money inside

Rita Where are you going, Shirl?
Shirley To the loo.
Rita Oh.

Shirley goes out through the door. Rita sits on a bale of straw, unknots her handkerchief and counts her money

Rita Shilling, one and three, one and fourpence, one and five, one and six, one and seven. What can we get for one and seven, Shirl? (*She wraps the money up again, sees and picks up the empty crisp pack*) You've eaten all the crisps. (*She throws the pack down, picks up the handbag, puts her handkerchief and money into it, pulls out a small mirror and lipstick, and starts to apply it rather badly*) Shirl.

Shirley returns

Shirley Stop shouting, you silly cow. Do you want everyone to hear?
Rita Sorry.

Shirley comes over to Rita and rudely snatches the lipstick and mirror

I've got one and seven. We could get a cup of tea and some crisps.
Shirley Where?
Rita There must be a caff or something near.
Shirley We're not going to no caff.
Rita But I'm hungry.
Shirley Honestly, Reet, you've got nothing above your neck. We'll spend the money in a supermarket.
Rita What for?
Shirley Well, you can't go into a supermarket and spend nothing, can you?
Rita No.
Shirley So, use your loaf. We go in there and spend the one and seven, and while we are in there we nick enough to keep ourselves going all day.
Rita Oh, Shirl.
Shirley It's as easy as pie.
Rita I don't want to get into no more trouble.
Shirley You're in trouble already, scarpering from school, so a little more won't make much difference. 'Sides, we won't get caught. It's dead easy.
Rita I don't know.

Shirley Oh, for God's sake, Reet. You aren't half chicken. We won't get caught I tell you.
Rita I'm sorry, Shirl. I wish I was as clever as you.
Shirley Well, you're not.

Rita gets up and moves over to the window, looking out

Rita Can't we get going?
Shirley Can you see anyone?
Rita No.

Shirley comes over to look

Shirley Look.
Rita What?
Shirley Over there. Those boys.
Rita They're miles away.
Shirley We'd better wait a bit. Keep watching and tell me what they do.

(*She comes away from the window and pokes about in the straw with her foot. She finds a dead mouse and utters an exclamation of disgust*)

Rita What's up?
Shirley There's a rat.
Rita (*joining her*) Let's have a look. Where?
Shirley Just down there by your foot.

Rita sees it and bends down to look at it

Rita That's not a rat. That's a mouse.
Shirley Same thing.
Rita Of course it's not. A mouse is much smaller.
Shirley Well, it gives me the creeps. Us sleeping there with that horrible thing. Don't touch it, Reet.
Rita It's dead.
Shirley Leave it alone.
Rita (*picking it up*) Oh, look, it's lovely. Poor little mouse. Look, Shirl, it's ever so pretty. Look at its sweet little face.
Shirley (*backing away in alarm*) Don't you come near me with that thing. It's horrible.
Rita It's not horrible. It's beautiful. (*She cradles the mouse in her hand and strokes its fur. Then she moves over to and sits on the upturned box*) Poor little mouse, why did you have to die? Why did you die, little mouse? I wish I had found you when you were alive. I would have looked after you and you wouldn't have died.
Shirley Don't be so daft. Throw it away.
Rita I always wanted a mouse. Cathie wouldn't let me have one. I wanted a mouse so much. Poor little thing. Why is God so cruel to make you die? (*She is emotionally moved and bites her lip to keep back the tears*)
Shirley Reet.
Rita I can't help it. I love it. I'm going to bury it properly.
Shirley You're so soft. Throw it away.

Rita No.

Rita moves towards the door, but Shirley moves quicker and bars her way

Shirley You can't go out there. Those boys.
Rita I'll keep it and bury it later.
Shirley (*looking out and through the door*) Rita, the boys. They're coming this way.
Rita Oh God, Shirl, what are we going to do? (*She moves to the window*)
Shirley Ssh! They may not come in.
Rita (*looking out*) Oh God!
Shirley Shut up.

For a few seconds the girls peer anxiously out of the window and door. Suddenly Shirley moves quickly

Quick. Under the straw.

They hurriedly try to bury themselves, using the sacks and tarpaulin

Throw that rat away.
Rita It's not a rat.
Shirley Throw the bloody thing away.
Rita No, no.

They scuffle. Shirley gets the mouse and throws it across the barn

I hate you.
Shirley Shut up.

They settle under the straw and keep quiet and still, apart from an occasional sniff by Rita

DAVID ROWLEY

THE KING'S MESSENGER

BETTY / FRANCES

The time is 1640. The place the farmyard of Sir John Field's country home. There is a scarecrow in evidence, dressed in an old cloak and feathered hat. Betty, Sir John Field's young daughter, is churning cream when Frances, a girl of her own age, enters quietly. Both girls are on the side of the Royalists

Betty fetches cream and pours it into a churn, and gets busy

Unseen by Betty, a girl appears at the gate and peers cautiously in, and hides as Betty looks up

In due course she decides that all is well, and walks carefully into the yard, standing back against the wall. If she can whistle softly to attract Betty she does so

Betty stops churning and stands away, surprised

Betty Who are you?
Frances Quietly, I pray you. My name is Frances. Whose house is this?
Betty Sir John Field's, Knight.
Frances Good! Who are you?
Betty Mistress Elizabeth Field, daughter of Sir John. Who are *you*?
Frances I need your help, in the King's name.
Betty In the King's name!
Frances Yes, and your father sent me.
Betty (*changing at once, all friends, eager*) From Father! You have news of him? Come and see Mother. Come into the house ... News from Father! (*She is about to call out*)
Frances (*coming downstage*) Hush! Listen, Mistress. I am in great haste. My father's best mare is tied in your orchard. I am riding to Oxford, to the Court, with a secret message to the King. You can help me.
Betty But you're only a girl ... and ...
Frances That's why they let me come. Better chance of getting through. My father is holding our Manor against the Parliament. Your father is there, and other gentry and three hundred men.
Betty Is Father well?
Frances Quite well. A brave gentleman—he is in command. The King is at Oxford, sixty miles away. I was given the message.
Betty Where is it?
Frances (*touching her hat*) Sewn in here. If it should fall into the hands of Parliament or Cromwell all will be lost. They thought I'd have a better chance of getting through than a man. (*Acting the simple schoolgirl*) I am a maiden travelling to my grandmama's house. My groom has broken his leg, so I am alone.

57

Betty Bravo! I'd give a fortune to have your luck. To play the man . . . messenger for the King—a King's Messenger! Can I come with you?

Frances One travels swifter than two. But, my reason for coming. Your father sends you his love, and his duty to your Lady Mother. He told me to tell you to fetch a ring from your mother's jewel box. It is a ring the King once gave him. I am to wear it, then I shall get through the King's lines, and to the King himself.

Betty (*fearing the worst*) A ring? What kind of a ring?

Frances He described it carefully. Two serpents, entwined, with a jewel in their mouths. Fetch it for me, and I must ride on.

Betty And *I* persuaded my mother. Alas!

Frances Why, what's amiss?

Betty That ring, of my father's—we have sold it, not half an hour since!

Frances Sold it? To whom?

Betty To an old pedlar woman who came round.

Frances A pedlar woman! (*Startled and quick*) Not a tall, bent woman, with a voice like this—

> Laces and ribbons,
> Tokens and charms,
> Newsheets and chaplets
> And all things of delight. . . .

Betty Yes, d'you know her? She's in—

Frances (*sitting down in despair and throwing her hat aside*) They warned me especially about her. She's a spy, one of Cromwell's most dangerous spies.

Betty A spy!

Frances We are lost. If she sees or suspects me she'll have a troop of Roundheads on me! And you have *sold her*, of all people, the ring, my pass to the King! Where is she? Which way did she go?

Betty (*seeing a reprieve, pleased*) She's not gone; she's in the house, with my mother.

Frances (*jumping up*) In the house! HERE?

Betty Yes. Shall I fetch her?

Frances No. We must act. Listen. I will hide (*She looks about her*) and you *must* buy that ring back. Then, when she has gone, I'll take it and trust to my father's mare and Providence to get away from her. Where shall I hide?

Betty In the barn?

Frances No. Better here, in the scarecrow. Help me, quickly—I hear voices.

Betty It's them.

The hat is left on the ground. Frances gets into the scarecrow's cloak and puts on the scarecrow's hat and stands stiffly, moving a little at first. Betty moves back to the churn

DAVID SCOTT DANIELL

LITTLE WOMEN

JO / AMY

When they grow up Jo and Amy become good friends. But in their youth Amy presents many difficulties for her older sister who wants the play she has written to be performed successfully. The scene is set in the parlour of the March family home, at Christmas time, mid-nineteenth century, in America

Jo Come on, Amy . . . we're going to do "The Curse of Hugo". That's a fine play with plenty of dramatic action.

Amy Is that the one where I have to faint when the villain comes in?

Jo Yes.

Amy I won't do it.

Jo Oh, come on Amy . . . Just this once.

Amy No . . . all your plays are stupid if you ask me.

Jo Just this once, Amy.

Amy Oh very well . . . just this once. But only because it's Christmas and I am full of the spirit of goodwill.

Jo Splendid! Come here and rehearse the fainting scene: you always were as stiff as a poker in that.

Amy Well, I can't help it. I never saw anybody faint, and I don't intend to make myself black and blue all over just because of a silly old play. If I can go down easily, I'll drop, and if I can't I shall fall gracefully into a chair, even if the villain does come at me with a pistol.

Jo Oh, don't be ridiculous. You can't faint into a chair, it's not realistic. Look—er—do it this way. Clasp your hands together—so. Then stagger across the room crying frantically "Roderigo! Roderigo! Save me—Save me!" Then you scream like this. (*She screams*) Now you do it.

Amy Roderigo! Roderigo! Save me . . . Save me! (*She gives a tiny "Ow"*)

Jo It's no use . . . you're hopeless! Oh well, I guess you'll have to do the best you can when the time comes. Now do the fainting bit.

Amy I've told you, I don't know how to.

Jo But it's so easy if you'll only try. You must relax and let your whole body go limp, then collapse onto the floor.

Amy tries to do this

Christopher Columbus, Amy, that's not a faint, it's a curtsy.

Amy I am sorry, it's the best I can do.

Jo Well, keep on trying. . . . Now . . . we shall need the steps . . . and a few props from the cupboard. Put this dress on Amy.

Amy It's too big.

Jo That doesn't matter. Put it on . . . and then climb the step ladder.

Amy puts the dress on. Jo puts on the sword belt and sword

Amy No, I don't want to, they're not safe.

Jo Of course they're safe.

Amy I'm not climbing those steps for you or anyone else, Jo March, and you can't make me.

Jo Oh, can't I? (*She points the sword at Amy*)

Amy Why, you great big bully, Jo March. It's downright cruelty, that's what it is making me climb up here. If I fall and hurt myself it will be your fault, and if I did you wouldn't come and visit me in hospital. . . . And why am I always the one who has to play those sort of parts . . . that's what I want to know . . . why not Meg or Beth?

Jo I'm not taking any notice of you Amy. You enjoy grumbling. Now, are you ready? The scene opens with the entrance of the wicked villain Hugo and then Roderigo the handsome hero enters and rescues Princess Zara from the tower in the castle, where Hugo is keeping her prisoner. You are Zara, Amy . . . so take that sulky expression off your face and try to look more like a Princess. Are we ready? Curtain up! . . . "Ha-Ha! Here is the deadly poison that will destroy my rival Roderigo. One drink from this bottle and he will be dead. While he is dining with Zara tonight I shall creep in and pour a large dose into his cup of wine."

Amy How is he going to do that without being seen?

Jo You're not supposed to ask that!

Amy Yes, but how does he?

Jo Amy, will you stop asking questions and keep to the script?

Amy I haven't got one.

Jo Then don't interrupt. Just sit there and keep quiet. And smile . . . look happy . . . you're supposed to be in love!

Amy smiles fixedly

That's better. . . . Now! "Exit Hugo, enter Roderigo".

She exits and re-enters, wearing a different hat, and kneels

Amy You've got a different hat on.

Jo Of course I've got a different hat on . . . I'm a different person. Oh, now you've ruined my entrance. For the last time Amy, will you please be quiet . . .?

Amy stares into space

"I have come to rescue thee, my love. Let us hasten away together before the wicked villain, Hugo, discovers our plot to escape."

She repeats the lines, Amy still does not hear

Amy, will you please concentrate? Whatever's the matter with you? You look as though you've got indigestion!

Amy It so happens that I do have indigestion.

Jo Amy! Now you descend the ladder slowly and carefully and Roderigo and Zara ride off into the moonlight on a beautiful white horse.

Amy I suppose you are playing the part of the horse as well.

Jo There isn't any horse. Oh, be quiet and start climbing down the ladder.

Amy climbs down the ladder and gets caught. She screams

You stupid child, you've ruined the entire scene!

Amy Well, I couldn't help it if my skirt's got caught up, and besides it was your fault for making me wear a dress that was miles too big. Anyway, it's a silly play. All your plays are silly and I'll never act in another one again!

Jo You certainly won't because I shan't give you the opportunity!

Adapted by SHEILA CORBETT
from Louisa Alcott

LIZZIE DRIPPING

LIZZIE / PATTY

Lizzie Dripping got her name because she seems to live in an imaginative world of her own. She tends to be always in trouble and thinks her parents prefer the new baby. Of course, no-one is likely to believe that she has met a witch . . .

In the first scene she is having one of her normal sessions with Patty, her long-suffering mother. In the second scene she meets the witch in the graveyard

Lizzie has been in trouble for losing her baby brother. Although he is now safely home her mother is still cross with her. Patty Arbuckle is rolling pastry and Lizzie is rummaging through a drawer

Lizzie Seen my box o' chalks, Mam? I want to play hopscotch.

Patty (*rolling with a will*) Don't you go chalking on our yard. You want to play hopscotch, you play it on pavement, where it belongs. Chalk on pavement out of my way.

Lizzie I can't chalk anywhere—that's the whole point. I keep telling you I can't find my chalks.

Patty And that don't surprise. If you can go losing your own brother, you can lose anything.

Lizzie (*aside*) Here we go again . . .

Patty Wonder to me is you've got your own head left on your shoulders. Lose that, I s'pose, if you'd half the chance.

Lizzie (*aside*) On and on about that dratted baby. Might've known she'd drag THAT into it.

Patty (*fetching a baking tin*) Pity, Lizzie, you can't find something useful to do, instead of forever standing about gawping. (*She returns to the table*)

Lizzie (*watching her*) Be all right if I knew what she EXPECTED me to do. After all, 't'Saturday. Holidays, I thought, Saturdays was meant to be. (*Loudly*) Is there any jobs you want doing, Mam?

Patty Well, I daresay there would be, if I could think. And if you was to be relied on, Lizzie. Look at that pound o' butter you left lying in grave-yard! I ask you—butter in't graveyard! I should think it's the only time there's been butter in't graveyard since world began.

Lizzie I ran straight back for it, Mam. Didn't come to no harm.

Batty That's not point, Lizzie. It's the very IDEA of it. (*She gives a mock shudder*) Nearly made me that I couldn't fancy it, knowing where it'd been.

Lizzie Well, is there anything else, then? Besides errands?

Patty (*crossly and irrationally*) Oh, do stop PURGING at me, Lizzie.

Lizzie (*aside*) First I annoy her doing nowt. Now she don't want me to do OWT. Can't do anything right. (*A pause. Her face brightens*) Go and pick

62

her a bunch of flowers. Aye, that's what . . . (*She goes to the door*) Shan't be a minute, Mam.

Lizzie exits

Patty goes on rolling pastry. Upstairs the baby is yelling
Patty Drat the child! If it ain't one of 'em it's 't' other. All right, all right I'm coming! (*She goes off to the bedroom*)

Lizzie peers cautiously round the door, then enters, holding a bunch of flowers

Lizzie Must 'a' gone up to Toby. Quick, where's that green vase that she likes? (*She goes to the cupboard and finds the vase*) That'll do. Look smashing they will, in there. (*She hears Patty returning*) Quick . . . she's coming. (*She starts to hurry and trips. The vase flies out of her hand and breaks just as Patty comes back. Lizzie wails*)
Patty (*horrified*) That's my vase! That's my best vase!
Lizzie (*equally horrified and near tears*) I was—I was putting flowers in it, for a surprise! (*She waves a bunch of flowers*) Oh, I'm sorry, Mam, I'm sorry.

Lizzie bends to pick up the pieces. Patty does not reply but gets pan and brush to sweep up the fragments

Patty Stand out t'road. Next thing, you'll have glass in your feet. (*She stands up, and looks at the contents of the pan*) That's that, then.
Lizzie I'm sorry, Mam, I'm sorry. I couldn't help it. I tripped.
Patty And had to pick my best vase to do it with. That's what beats me. Couldn't have done it with a jam jar or that old brown pot o' your grandma's. You drive me to distraction, Lizzie, I swear you do. You can't be turned back of five minutes together. That baby's more trusted to be left than you.

Patty exits and the rattle of glass as she empties the pan can be heard off stage

Lizzie (*moving disconsolately to a chair*) She wouldn't carry on like this if she knew I'd got a witch for friend.

Patty returns, puts pan and brush away, and continues pastry-making tight-lipped

She'd look out what she said to me if she knew that. Shall I tell? (*She pulls a face and shakes her head*) Fat lot o' good that'd do. Don't suppose she even believes in witches . . . (*Her face suddenly brightens*) I know what! I'll go and see if witch is there. And if she is, I might get her to do a spell. What if she could do a spell so's Mam'd never find fault with me ever again? (*Smiling at the thought she rises, and says casually*) Just off for a bit, Mam.

Patty shrugs

Lizzie exits

HELEN CRESSWELL

LIZZIE DRIPPING

LIZZIE / WITCH

The scene: A graveyard. Lizzie enters, running at first, then cautiously

Lizzie Let her be there. Let my witch be there. Better go careful now. Better see her afore she sees me. (*Pause. Softly*) Witch. . .! (*Pause. A little louder*) Witch! Witch, where are you? (*Pause. She looks about her*) Could be playing hide-and-seek I suppose. Seemed like that kind of a witch.

Witch (*hidden, either on or offstage*) I spy, I spy with my little eye.

Lizzie jumps and looks round nervously

I see you!

Lizzie (*still wary*) Well, I don't see you.

Witch (*cackling*) Couldn't if you tried! Invisible!

Lizzie (*pleading*) Couldn't you come visible, please? Just for a minute. (*Pause. She looks round again*) Please?

She screams as the Witch appears

Witch (*with satisfaction*) That made you jump. What d'you want now?

Lizzie (*faltering*) Well . . . er . . . (*Aside*) Can't come straight out with it, not just like that. (*Aloud*) Well—er—for one thing, I wondered what your name was?

Witch Not telling.

Lizzie (*taken aback*) Oh!

Witch (*arranging herself on a grave slab and taking out her knitting*) Don't want folks yelling my name all over from morning till night. Might be invisible, but I ain't deaf, and if there's one thing I detest it's having folks yelling my name all over.

Lizzie I'm sorry. All right, Witch, don't tell me, not if you don't want. But I did just wonder . . . Well, I wondered if you'd do a little spell for me. Just a little one . . .

Witch (*hoity-toity*) There ain't such things as little spells. Spells is big. ALL spells is big.

Lizzie (*faltering*) Well, then, a big one, please Witch. But it ain't a bad one—not a wicked one—that's what I meant.

Witch (*putting her knitting away*) What, then?

Lizzie (*carefully*) It's to do wi' my Mam, see. Gone off me lately, she has. Telling me off the whole time—you know . . .

Witch (*not looking up*) Why?

Lizzie (*shrugging*) Dunno. Not my fault. Mostly because I left that dratted baby in't mill. Lot o' fuss. Anyone could've made a mistake like that.

Witch What spell d'ye want, then? (*Looking up with sudden interest*) Turn baby into toad, shall I?

Lizzie Oh no! (*Horrified*) Don't do that, please.

Witch (*momentarily disappointed, then her face becomes gleeful again*) Mam, then. Turn her to toad, shall I?

Lizzie (*aghast at what she might have started*) Oh, no, no. Oh, you've got it all wrong. I don't want ANYONE turning toad. All I want is for you to make a spell to make Mam like me a bit more, and not always be . . .

The Witch disappears and Lizzie breaks off in surprise

Oh, now I've gone and done it!

Witch (*reappearing and snapping out*) Do it yourself! (*She disappears again*)

Lizzie (*after a pause. Uncertainly*) Witch? Witch, are you still there? (*Pause*) I bet you are. . . . So listen, please do. I just wanted to put a spell on Mam so's to make her . . . well . . . you know . . . LIKE me a bit more. Take more notice, instead of being always on about Toby. Never calls ME her little petty pie. . . . Witch . . . Witch? . . . (*Pause*) She ain't coming back, I know it. Not if I was to wait all day and all night . . . (*Beginning to turn away*) Even the witch don't like me any more. Nobody cares. Nobody in the whole world.

Witch (*from offstage, or poking head round swiftly*) Do it yourself!

Lizzie whirls round but sees nothing. After a moment she draws herself up

Lizzie (*loudly, for Witch to hear, and determinedly*) All right, I WILL do it myself . . .! And I know what I'll do too. I'll get lost. I'll run away, that's what I'll do. And then they'll realize how much they love me, and be sorry. And they'll make a fuss over me, like they did Toby when he got lost, and Mam'll never tell me off again for the whole of the rest of my life . . . not for ANYTHING. (*She nods and smiles with satisfaction as off she goes*)

HELEN CRESSWELL

LIZARD IN THE GRASS

CLARE / JANE

Jane Pace is a strange, lonely girl at a convent school on the East Coast of England. Her mind is filled with poetry and odd ideas. She does not "fit in". An orphan, she is remaining at the school for the half-term holiday. Clare, a girl in her class, makes one more effort to break through the barrier

Clare What are you doing?

Jane Nothing.

Clare I shall have to sit on my case.

Jane Yes.

Clare We're going home. (*Pause*) If I sit on it, will it break? The hinges might break. (*Pause*) I wonder what you'll do here. What will it be like, just with them? Sister Imelda might let you go out and take food to the birds. You can get round her, you might be O.K.

Jane I don't mind.

Clare They might give you cake for tea.

Jane It's all right.

Clare Well, I can't shut my case . . . I can't take anything out. I need everything.

Jane (*very quietly*) "That when ye think all danger for to pass,
Ware of the lizard lieth lurking in the grass."

Clare What? Anyway, Sister Imelda's all right I've told you, just ask her. About the birds. You're always going on about them. Just try asking her, why don't you?

Jane (*amused*) What are you worrying about me for? I don't mind. I don't mind anything.

Clare What'll you do? It'll all be empty. Everywhere. Well, except for them.

Jane I don't care.

Clare You will.

Jane You'll be the last. Your case won't shut.

Clare Look, I'm only trying to be nice to you, Jane Pace. I'm only risking getting into a row, that's all . . . you're not supposed to be spoken to in case you didn't know.

Jane I wish you'd all be gone.

Clare Anyway, you've got to learn *The Lady of Shalott* . . . all of it. That'll take you about all week, I should think.

Jane I know it.

Clare They'll make you go to Chapel all day and take long healthy walks.

Jane There are bones on the beach. Did you know?

Clare Shall I take my French book out? Then I might be able to shut it.

Jane How queer you all look, buzz buzz buzzing about . . . all in brown and yellow. And only I am still.

66

Clare They won't let you go near the beach, anyway, you nearly got expelled for that before. You'll have to walk round and round and round the tennis court with a book, all on your own. Like they do, when they're saying Office. Perhaps they'll make you go with them and say it as well. Perhaps they'll try and make you promise to be a nun.

Jane I shall go down the cliff path and on to the beach and walk by the
, sea. I shall go into the ruins and look for the well . . .

Clare You'll get sent away for ever.

Jane I can do anything. I can do what I want.

Clare They'll lock you up.

Jane I could walk a hundred miles along the beach and never come back. I could find things. There are bones on the beach.

Clare (*hearing Megan calling*) Oh . . . Coming . . .
   "No more walking round the garden
   Always begging Sister's pardon.
   No more spiders in my tea, making googly eyes at me",
I wish it wasn't only half term. I wish it wasn't only a week. Coming! Jane . . .

Jane Go on. Go away.

Clare Jane . . .

Jane Go away . . .

Clare goes

I am me. I can do anything.

SUSAN HILL

MADDY ALONE

MADDY / MRS FANE

Maddy, at twelve years old, feels resentful because her sister and friends, all older, have gone away to Drama School in London. Left in Fenchurch, she makes life difficult for her parents. The scene is breakfast-time, on a school morning, in the mid-forties

Mrs Fayne (*having set the table*) Maddy! Get up! You're late already and your breakfast is getting cold! This is the third time I've called you!

Maddy (*off*) I am up. (*Looking at herself in the hall glass*) Oh, WHY am I only twelve? Why do the others always do all the exciting things before me? Horrid old tunic! Beastly old stockings.

Making a foul face at herself, she tidies her pigtails, and enters the dining-room

Mrs Fayne Oh, here you are at last. I thought you must have got sleeping sickness.

Maddy (*growling*) I wish I had.

Mrs Fayne Now, don't be naughty, Maddy dear. Do hurry up and eat your breakfast. Did you do your arithmetic eventually last night?

Maddy No, Mummy.

Mrs Fayne But won't you get into trouble?

Maddy Yes, Mummy.

Mrs Fayne I really don't know what's come over you since the others went away. I've never seen you so bad-tempered. You really must pull yourself together. Whatever will Sandra think of you?

Maddy (*drawing patterns in the porridge*) I really don't care what she thinks.

Mrs Fayne (*sharply*) Really, Maddy, I despair of you. I shall tell your father what a naughty girl you're being.

Maddy And what could he do about it?

Mrs Fayne He could stop your pocket money and then you wouldn't waste it on going to the cinema all the time.

Maddy But it's Deanna Durbin's new film next week. Oh, Mummy, you are horrid. You know I want to see it.

Mrs Fayne Well, you'll have to improve a lot if you're to be allowed to go. (*Firmly*) The first thing to be done is that arithmetic! (*She finds Maddy's book*) Are these the ones?

Maddy Yes. But it's no good. I can't do them.

Mrs Fayne You can if you try. Now here we are. Listen. It's quite easy. 'If three men, A, B and C, have to dig a field one acre in size, and A does one-twelfth, and B does eight-fifteenths, what does C do?

Maddy Goes on strike, I should think.

68

Mrs Fayne (*pleading*) Oh, Maddy dear, please try to concentrate. That's not funny. No wonder all your teachers complain about you.

Maddy (*complacently*) Some of them quite like me.

Mrs Fayne They wouldn't if they saw you at home. I sometimes wish you'd gone away with the others.

Maddy YOU wish I had! How do you think I feel about it? Here am I learning about horrible men digging beastly fields when Sandra and all the others are learning all the things I want to know. I'm not interested in fields, or digging, or arithmetic, or algebra, or geometry, or spelling, or anything they teach me at school. I'm wasting my time—that's what I'm doing—I'm wasting the best years of my life. Youth is passing me by while I sit at a desk wearing a stuffy gym-tunic. (*She bursts into tears of self pity*) Well, I'm not going to any longer, so there! I'm not even going to school any more and you can't make me, and if you try to I shall do something terrible, so that you'll be sorry for ever after!

Mrs Fayne Maddy! How can you be so naughty!

Maddy (*screaming*) I'm not naughty! I'm not naughty! I'm just unhappy and nobody cares. You don't care, nor does Daddy, or Sandra, or Jeremy, or Nigel, or anyone, not even the Bishop. (*She weeps bitterly at the thought of this*)

Mrs Fayne And what would the Bishop say if he were to see you now? He'd be sorry he ever let you play in the Blue Door Theatre and took you to Stratford-on-Avon. In fact, if I see the Bishop in the town this morning I shall tell him what a wicked girl you're being.

Maddy (*gasping, horrified*) Oh, Mummy! You COULDN'T do that . . .

Mrs Fayne I most certainly shall.

Maddy (*with fresh tears*) I shall never forgive you if you do. I'll—I'll go upstairs and lock myself in my room and I won't come out until you promise not to tell the Bishop about me.

Mrs Fayne (*assuming a nonchalant air*) I'm sure I don't care HOW long⋅ you stay there. You'll get into trouble for not going to school this morning but I know you'll come down when you're hungry.

Maddy (*shouting*) I shan't! I'll starve, and then you'll be sorry . . .

Mrs Fayne (*airily*) Oh, no I shan't. I should be quite pleased if you lost a little puppy fat.

Maddy Oh, you're horrid . . . you're horrid. And I won't come down from my room. (*She rushes to the door*) Never! (*And she slams the door as she goes*)

PAMELA BROWN

THE NAUGHTY GIRLS

THELMA / ELIZABETH

This comes from a crime thriller. Thelma and Elizabeth, small girls on holiday in the South of France become involved with two holidaymakers, who turn out to be criminals. Thelma has led Elizabeth into prying, eavesdropping and taking incriminating photographs, but now Elizabeth is scared and wants to back out and forget it

Elizabeth What do you want?
Thelma Do you want to play?
Elizabeth No.
Thelma Why not?
Elizabeth I don't like you. You're not my friend.
Thelma Yes, I am. We've been—doing things—together.
Elizabeth Don't say that. I'm not doing anything else with you.
Thelma Do THEY know?
Elizabeth God, no. They'd die.
Thelma I don't think they ought to know.
Elizabeth They won't know . . . unless somebody tells them . . .
Thelma No.
Elizabeth You wouldn't!
Thelma I don't expect so.
Elizabeth What do you want?
Thelma Richard's done the pictures. Do you want to see them?
Elizabeth No, I don't. I don't want anything to do with them. And I don't like you.
Thelma You took the money. You took fifty francs for the other picture.
Elizabeth I'm going to give it back. I'm going to tell them—and I'm going to say I'm sorry.
Thelma Tell them? Everything?
Elizabeth Yes.
Thelma I expect they'll be cross when they know.
Elizabeth 'Course they will. I know. But it's not fair. I like Bob.
Thelma Will you just tell them about you? Or about me as well?
Elizabeth I'll have to say we both did it. I'll HAVE to, won't I? They won't believe I did it by myself.
Thelma You could say it was someone else. Just SOMEONE . . . not with a name.
Elizabeth But they'd know, wouldn't they? They know you're my friend. WERE my friend. They'd know it was you even if I didn't say a name.
Thelma I expect so.
Elizabeth Listen, why don't we both tell them?
Thelma All right.

Elizabeth You will?

Thelma All right.

Elizabeth Oh, God, I'm so glad. We can tell them everything, and they'll be livid and we'll say we're sorry, and they'll say it's just because we're little girls and never mind so long as we've learnt our lesson and we can give them back the photographs and it'll all be over.

Thelma It'll all be over.

Elizabeth Then we can be friends again. I'll be so glad. It's been AWFUL this afternoon remembering the bed and Bob looking everywhere and nearly finding us. Remembering you weren't my friend any more.

Thelma Of course I'm your friend.

Elizabeth I'm so GLAD. But, God, what WILL Bob say?

Thelma He'll be cross, I expect.

Elizabeth But then it will all be over won't it? Oh, God, I'll be so glad. And we can be friends again and we can be friends with Bob when he gets over it. Have you got the photos?

Thelma In my handbag.

Elizabeth Haven't you got your sunglasses?

Thelma In my handbag.

Elizabeth Do you carry everything in your handbag?

Thelma Yes. I don't expect they'll be up.

Elizabeth I hadn't thought.

Thelma They weren't dressed yesterday.

Elizabeth What shall we do?

Thelma Wait.

Elizabeth I don't really mind waiting. I don't really WANT to tell Bob. 'Course we'll have to. . . . I wish we'd never done it.

Thelma You want to see the pictures again?

Elizabeth If you like. . . . It'll be the last time, won't it?

Thelma I expect so.

Elizabeth (*looking at the photographs*) Good Lord.

Thelma You're going to tell them everything, aren't you?

Elizabeth Yes. (*Looking at the photographs still*) But I don't want to.

Thelma Why are you going to tell them if you don't want to?

Elizabeth I've got to. That's what I said. I told you. I've got to. I don't WANT to . . . but I don't feel . . . you know . . . CLEAN . . .

Thelma Have you made up your mind?

Elizabeth Of course. (*She puts the photographs in her pocket*)

Thelma I want them.

Elizabeth If I'm going to tell them, I'll have to show them. You can keep the others . . . the negatives . . .

Thelma All right. If you've made up your mind. (*She puts her hand in her bag*)

Elizabeth Do you expect they'll be up yet?

Thelma I expect they might be.

Elizabeth Oh, well, let's get it over with.

Thelma We're not going to tell them . . .

Elizabeth But, Thelma . . . you said . . .

Thelma I wouldn't have told them. I wouldn't ever have told them. . . . But
you said you were going to tell them . . . and you were going to tell them
about me . . .
Elizabeth Thelma, don't joke. . . . Please.

Thelma does not answer. She takes a revolver out of her handbag

I thought we were friends.
Thelma We're not.
Elizabeth Thelma, please! You can have anything you want. I'll give you
anything. I won't tell them. I didn't mean it. Please don't shoot. You
might hurt me.

*Thelma shoots. Elizabeth falls to the ground. Thelma looks about her, then,
after a pause, covers the body with dead leaves. She picks up the gun, then
wipes it on her hanky, and hides it in the leaves*

Carrying her bag she goes off

Adapted from the novel by
ARTHUR WISE

NIGHT CHILD

KATE / JESSIKA

I saw a compelling production of this musical play at the Young Vic Theatre, London, in 1978, performed by the girls of Queen's College School for whom it was written. The action chiefly takes place in the dormitory of a girls' boarding school during the Summer term. Kate is disturbed by dreams and influenced by her readings of ancient ritual and sacrifice. Her friends do try to understand her but find her behaviour wearing

If the girl playing Jessika is not a blonde, it helps to tell the audience that she is meant to be

Scene: the school dormitory. Kate is reading alone. Jessika enters

Jessika Hi.
Kate Hi.
Jessika You can't still have homework to do. It's the last day of term.
Kate No. I'm just reading.
Jessika You're always reading those books you brought back.

Kate smiles. Jessika sits down and flicks through a pop magazine

    Kate?
Kate Mm?
Jessica You know you've changed so much since you've been back.
Kate How do you mean?
Jessika Oh, I don't know. You've been so much calmer. (*Pause*) It just proves what a good thing it was that you went after all. (*Silence*) Kate, what did the doctors say that made so much difference?
Kate It wasn't the doctors.
Jessika Well, whoever. What did they say?
Kate (*looking up. Pause*) Oh—it's difficult to explain.
Jessika Oh, go on, try. I'll understand.

Pause

Kate O.K. I'd like you to understand—but you've got to listen to it all the way through.
Jessika O.K.
Kate (*hesitantly. She is thinking carefully as she speaks. She grows in confidence as she goes on*) Well—before—I suppose the real thing wrong with me was that I was scared all the time—you know—scared of being different from other people—about what those dreams meant—about what was going to happen to me. ... I didn't realize that—that—being frightened—is really just not understanding about something. And

73

I suppose that what I was *really* frightened of was—was—dying—and that was because I didn't understand what death was . . .

Jessika Why all this talk of . . . (*She was going to say "of dying"*)

Kate No. Don't interrupt. You promised to listen all the way through. I didn't understand that everything has got to have its opposite. There can't be any light without darkness. There can't be any day without night. (*More brightly*) It's like you and me really—we're opposites of each other. That's why we get on so well. (*Pause*) And one day all these opposites come together, and something fantastic happens. (*More excitedly*) An explosion or something. Like when the sun bursts over the horizon. It's always the *beginning* of something *new*. And that's what dying is really—and that's why it's nothing to be frightened of (*Looks at Jessika. Pause*) Well?

Jessika (*ominously*) Have you finished now?

Kate Yes.

Jessika Well, I think it's ridiculous. I think it's morbid, all this talk of dying. No-one's going to die. God, I really think you're worse than before. At least you never used to talk like this. I'd prefer you screaming to sitting there smiling and brooding about death all the time. You're obsessed by it. (*Kate is sitting motionless*) What's this you're reading? (*Seizing her book*) I bet it's all the same rubbish.

Kate No, don't read that.

Jessika Why not? (*Looking at her book*) Yes. Listen to this . . .

During this long passage there is a slow lighting change leaving only one light from above on Jessika, lighting her very fair hair. Jessika begins by being ironic, mocking, but she soon becomes interested in what the book says, and reads just like a normal recitation, until finally disgusted at the end

(*Reading*) "By no people does the custom of human sacrifice, without which, it was believed, the new crop would surely fail, appear to have been observed with greater regularity than by the Aztecs, whose rituals were fully described by the Spaniards who conquered Mexico in the sixteenth century. At the great annual festival they sacrificed a young slave girl of twelve or thirteen to represent the corn goddess. They selected wherever possible, a fair girl, such as were relatively common among the early inhabitants of Central America and they decorated her yellow hair with corn stalks in order to make the identification complete. Thus she became the Mexican counterpart of Persephone who was carried away to the Underworld by Pluto; a golden headed bride for the Prince of Darkness. The whole long day (*Turns page*) dancing wildly from house to house, they led the poor girl in all her finery. At the end of the ceremony was this. The multitude being assembled, the priests solemnly anointed the girl; then they threw her on her back on a heap of corn and seeds, cut off her head, and caught the gushing blood——" Earggh—this is revolting. God, I feel sick. You really *are* mad to read this muck, or, if you weren't to begin with you will be by now. (*Shouting*) Anyway, you'd be dead useless by the sound of it. (*Turning to the back page*) "Golden headed bride", "prettiest girl they could find". It doesn't sound as if *you*'ve got anything to worry about.

She throws the book down and stalks out

A pause

Kate No—it isn't me—it isn't me. It's you.

SHANKARA ANGADI

THE RAILWAY CHILDREN

ROBERTA / MOTHER

Roberta and her family are living in a house near a railway in Yorkshire while Father is mysteriously "away". Money is short and their lives are altered. Roberta is the eldest and she has felt for some time that the truth has been kept for her, and here she finds that she was right. Time: 1906

Roberta (Bobbie) is sitting by the fire, reading a newspaper. Her hands and feet feel cold, her face burning. She draws a long breath

Bobbie So now I know. GUILTY. FIVE YEARS PENAL SERVITUDE. (*Whispering*) Oh, Daddy, it's not true. I don't believe it. You never did it! Never, never, never! (*A knock*) What is it?

Mother (*outside*) It's Mother. Is anything wrong, Bobbie?

Bobbie (*running to the door and opening it*) Come in. Come where nobody can hear us . . .

Mother What is it, darling . . .? Bobbie . . .?

But Bobbie is quite still, she can say nothing for a while. Then, she runs to her mother, puts her arms round her and cries

Bobbie Oh, Mammy, oh, Mammy, oh, Mammy. (*Suddenly she runs to her bed and gets the paper, pointing to her father's name*)

Mother (*after a quick look*) Oh, Bobbie, you don't BELIEVE it? You don't believe Daddy did it?

Bobbie (*almost shouting*) NO!

Mother That's all right. It's not true. And they've shut him up in prison, but he's done nothing wrong. He's good and noble and honourable and he belongs to us. We have to think of that, and be proud of him, and wait.

Bobbie (*clinging to her mother*) Oh, Daddy, Daddy, Daddy . . . (*After a moment*) Why didn't you tell me, Mammy?

Mother Are you going to tell the others?

Bobbie No.

Mother Why?

Bobbie Because . . .

Mother Exactly. So you understand why I didn't tell you. We two must help each other to be brave.

Bobbie Yes. . . . Mother, will it make you more unhappy if you tell me all about it? I want to understand.

Mother Well, you remember those men who came to see Daddy . . . before we came down here?

Bobbie Yes, when Daddy was in the middle of mending Peter's engine.

Mother That night. Well, they came to arrest Daddy. They charged him with selling State secrets to the Russians . . . with being a spy and a traitor.

Bobbie Not Daddy!

Mother Yes, Bobbie. There was a trial, and some letters were found in his desk at the Office, letters that convinced the jury that Father was guilty.

Bobbie Oh, how could they look at him and believe it! And how could ANYone do such a thing?

Mother SOMEONE did it, and all the evidence was against Father. Those letters . . .

Bobbie Yes. How did the letters get into his desk?

Mother Someone put them there. And the person who put them there was the person who was really guilty.

Bobbie HE must be feeling pretty awful all this time.

Mother (*hotly*) I don't believe he had any feelings . . . he couldn't have done a thing like that if he had.

Bobbie Perhaps he just shoved the letters into the desk to hide them when he thought he was going to be found out. Why don't you tell the lawyers, or someone, that it must have been that person? There wasn't anyone that would have hurt Father on purpose, was there?

Mother I don't know . . . I don't know. The man under him who got Daddy's place when he—when the awful thing happened—he was always jealous of your Father because Daddy was so clever and everyone thought such a lot of him. And Daddy never quite trusted that man.

Bobbie Couldn't we explain all that to someone?

Mother (*bitterly*) Nobody will listen . . . nobody at all. Do you suppose I've not tried everything? No, my dearest, there's nothing to be done. All we can do, you and I and Daddy, is to be brave, and patient, and (*very softly*) to pray, Bobbie dear.

Bobbie (*rather abruptly*) Mother, you've got very thin.

Mother A little perhaps.

Bobbie And oh, I do think you're the bravest person in the world as well as the nicest!

Mother We won't talk of all this any more, will we dear? We must bear it and be brave. And, darling, try not to think of it. It's much easier for me if you can be a little bit happy and enjoy things. Wash your poor face, and let's go out in the garden for a bit.

E. NESBIT

THE RIVER

HARRIET / BEA

Harriet and Bea, with their family, live in Bengal, India, where the rhythm of that country, its people, festivals and especially the river are as vital as their own English background. Both girls are affected by their friendship with Captain John, a soldier who has been invalided in the war. Harriet, twelve, wants to be a writer, and is perhaps less reserved than fourteen-year-old Bea

It is night time

Harriet Bea.
Bea SShhh.
Harriet Bea.
Bea What is it, Harriet? I am asleep.
Harriet Bea . . . When we are dead . . . Do we go . . . Like the guinea pig . . . Like Bathsheba?
Bea How did she go?
Harriet Stiff. Hard. Stinking.
Bea Yes, I suppose we do. . . . That is called a corpse. (*She lies down again*)
Harriet Bea . . . Bea . . . Bea . . . BEA.
Bea Oh, Harriet, I am asleep. What is it?
Harriet Bea. I don't want to.
Bea Don't want to what?
Harriet Be a corpse.
Bea But you are not.
Harriet But I shall be.
Bea Don't you think you could wait till you are? I am so sleepy, Harriet.

Harriet is crying

Couldn't you wait till the morning, Harry?
Harriet No. No. I can't . . . I am frightened, Bea. I can't get the feeling of Bathsheba off my hands . . . I am frightened, Bea.
Bea Don't cry . . . don't cry, Harry. It isn't anything to cry about. I'm sure it isn't
Harriet But Mother must die . . . and Nan . . . and Nan is old and must die quite soon. Why isn't it something to cry about?
Bea Oh, Harry, you ask too many questions.
Harriet Yes, but . . . don't you ever think about dying, Bea?
Bea Well, yes I do.
Harriet Then what do you think?
Bea It is hard to know what I think . . . But I KNOW a few things.
Harriet Wh—what do you know? . . . Nan and Mother and Ram Prasad tell us things about Heaven and Jesus and Brahmo, but they don't really know.

Bea I think they are all wrong. Mine are not things like that. They are more simple things. More sensible things.

Harriet What sort of things?

Bea This. When anything . . . anybody . . . is dead, like Bathsheba, it is dead. The life . . . the breath . . . the WARM in it is gone.

Harriet Nan calls it the spirit.

Bea The spirit then. I call it the Warm . . . but the spirit or the Warm is gone.

Harriet Yes . . . yes . . . it was gone out of Bathsheba.

Bea The body is left behind, and what happens to it? It goes bad.

Harriet Don't.

Bea You can't keep a body.

Harriet Except mummies . . . and those Rajahs that are pickled in honey.

Bea Then I think . . . then I *know*, that it isn't meant to go on. It is useless. The body isn't any use any more.

Harriet Yes?

Bea But the other, the warm, has gone. It doesn't stay and go bad. So I think that it is of some use. That it has gone to something, somewhere.

Harriet But where? where?

Bea You ask too many questions, Harry.

Harriet I wonder what Captain John thinks?

Bea Captain John?

Harriet Yes. He would think of something . . . what do you feel like with Captain John, Bea?

Bea gets into bed

I will learn more about it as I grow . . . Living and dying . . . and being born . . . like Captain John said. . . . Bea . . . Bea . . . Bea . . .

There is no answer. Bea is asleep. Harriet goes to sleep too

RUMMER GODDEN

THE RUNAWAY

CLARICE / OLGA

The was written in 1872. Clarice, a young girl of 'respectable upbringing' has secretly been hiding and caring for the younger Olga, but now she has learnt something that charges her attitude to the mischievous talkative little runaway. At this point in the story she finds Olga asleep in her bed

Clarice (*going to the bed, and putting down the candle*) Olga, get up!

Olga (*opening her eyes*) Oh you dear, Clarice! I am so glad you have come! I was so lonely that I went to sleep.

Clarice (*ignoring the upturned face*) You are discovered! I know all about you—who you are, and what you have been doing. You are a wicked girl, and you must go away from this!

Olga (*smiling*) Oh no! I'm not really wicked. I make-believe much worse than I am; and I won't THINK of going away, dear Clarice!

Clarice (*upset*) Olga, don't talk in this way, I can't bear it. You must go away; and you must leave the money and jewels behind you. I can't let you take them with you.

Olga (*laughing* Why, then, Clarice, it's YOU that are wicked, only I know you're not, because you're PARTICULARLY good. But fancy you turning me out of doors and keeping all my things! Why, you'd be a thief. Clarice!

Clarice Olga, YOU are a thief! And I know it! How dare you use that word when you are the thing itself?

Olga (*innocently, but scornful*) I am not a thief!

Clarice Don't, Olga—don't! You are adding to your sins by each word you say. I know everything, and you can't deceive me. They have advertised for you!

Olga My goodness! Advertised for ME!

Clarice There is a reward offered.

Olga (*beginning to laugh*) What fun! Oh, do tell me; what am I worth? What's my price, Clarice?

Clarice Olga, you make me shudder. Don't, pray don't. I know that you are a servant and a thief . . . it is all in the paper. You can't deceive me. Pray confess everything at once, and let us have done with it.

Olga I a servant and a thief. Fancy a Leslie being a servant and a thief

Clarice But you are not a Leslie. You are a servant, and you have told me nothing but falsehoods. What is you real name?

Olga My name is Olga Leslie.

Clarice Well, of course it may be Olga Leslie, but it is very unlikely.

Olga And it is EXTREMELY unlikely that yours is Clarice Clavering! I don't know one bit what you mean. Clarice, but of course you DON'T mean that I'm a thief, because that would be such nonsense. Ladies are

80

never thieves, of course. What do you mean by a thief? Do you mean a person who steals?

Clarice (*quietly*) Yes! I mean a person that steals.

Olga But you don't mean that *I* have stolen anything?

Clarice Yes, I do. I mean that you have stolen that money and those jewels you keep in your bag, and have run away from school—in which you were a servant, and that there is an advertisement in the newspapers telling all about it.

Olga (*looking earnestly into Clarice's eyes*) It's not true. It's a wicked advertisement made by some bad old person. Oh, Clarice, how COULD you believe it!

Clarice (*after a long hard stare at Olga*) Oh, Olga! dear little Olga! (*Crying*) Poor innocent little Olga! Oh, forgive me! Forgive me!

The two clasp each other, both crying now

Olga How could you Clarice? How could you believe anything horrid about poor little me? I couldn't believe anything against YOU. Not if all the bishops came to me in their aprons and SWORE to it. Because I know and I love you . . . so I couldn't; and to think I was a thief. Oh, Clarice, why a thief is worse than anybody else. I'd rather be a murderer for he's not so mean.

Clarence Forgive me, Olga . . . dear, dear Olga, forgive me.

Olga Oh, to be sure I forgive you . . . one can never help forgiving, can one But what could make anybody say such things about me in an advertisement? What a bad old person it must be! And what do they say, dear? Do they give my name?

Clarice No, they don't give your name. They say something about you having absconded from school in the North of England with stolen money and jewels to the amount of more than £50. And they say you are about 15, a sort of upper servant and junior teacher, short and slight dressed in grey cloak and straw bonnet . . .

Olga But what a horrid shame. Why, the money is what Grandmama sent me; and she gave me the jewels too. They belonged to her favourite daughter who died . . . so I didn't like leaving them behind me. And then to say I stole them! How very VERY wicked grown-up people are, Clarice.

Clarice And there is a five pound note and a pearl ring you left in the glade, and a man has found them and given them to the police.

Olga What! Half my money, and my pretty pearl ring. Oh what a shame! why, then, the man is the real thief AND the police! Oh, Clarice, do do you think WE could get the reward by giving up that man and the police instead of me?

Clarice (*laughing with Olga*) Oh, Olga, I am so sorry, but I am so glad . . . Oh, so very glad.

Olga Yes. It's just as well I'm not a thief for all parties; and what can make them say I'm a servant and a teacher? A Leslie a servant! And as to being a teacher—why, I'm sure I never taught anybody anything in my life, and for a very good reason too. I couldn't Why I don't know anything well enough to teach it—it would be a wise school that hired me as a teacher—wouldn't it, Clarice?

Clarice I do think, Clarice, that we must do something now—it will be dreadful if you are found out here, they'll want to put you in prison, and you're not steady enough to hide. You're sure to be found out. I think the best plan will be for you to write to your Grandmama and tell her all about it, and then she'll let you know what you are to do; and she might write and tell Papa. It is of no use for US to tell him now, because they are all persuaded that the advertisement is true.

Olga But Grandma is not at home.

Clarice Yes, but if you direct it home and put TO BE FORWARDED on the direction it will be sent to her.

Olga (*reluctantly*) Well, I suppose I must; but Grandmama won't be at all pleased, and half the good of being here will be gone when I've told. It is so nice being somewhere when everybody thinks you're nowhere at all.

ANNA ELIZABETH HART

THE TREASURE IN THE WITCHBALL

POLLY / CORISANDE

Two scenes from an unpublished play. The story is this: Princess Corisande has given her laughter to Old Martha of Mumping Moor in return for the removal of an unsightly blemish. With the help of Polly, her country maid, and Festus, the Court Jester she decides to try to get back her laughter, to prevent the Dumps (grey dismal shapes) from plaguing her.

In the first scene she and Polly are at the Crossroads, tired and worried

Corisande The signpost again. We must be walking in circles or else we are bewitched. I wish Festus had not left us.

Polly Him. A nice one he is. Leaving 'ee all alone wi' witches and Dumps and what-not.

Corisande (*flaring up*) He had to go. This is my quest. I alone can find my quest. Only I don't find it. And the Dumps keep coming. . . .

Polly (*driving the Dumps away*) Shoo. Be off now.

Corisande It's no use. They'll come back. They always do. And I *can't* find the witchball. I don't believe I ever shall.

Polly Give it up, love, and let's go home.

Corisande And do without laughter all my life?

Polly 'ee can do without most thing if 'ee must.

Corisande Perhaps. I'm so tired, Polly. . . . (*She sits on a log, leaning against Polly*)

Polly (*holding her*) Rest awhile: sleep awhile. Then us'll go home.

Corisande (*drowsily*) It's getting late. How lovely to sleep in my own bed to-night.

Festus (*heard singing off-stage*)
    How many miles to Mumping Moor?
      Three score and ten.
    Can I get there by candlelight?
      Yes and back again. . . . (*the singing dies away*)

Corisande (*starting up*) That was Festus. What are we doing here? We must go on.

Polly Best go home.

Corisande No. We must go on.

Polly Much good going on if we don't know the way.

Corisande We must find the way (*She goes to the signpost*) Polly, do you see? The signpost points between the paths.

Polly Aye. That be the trouble.

Corisande But don't you see? That's our way. Neither the right hand path nor the left, but between them.

83

Polly Cross Mumping Moor where there bain't even a path?

Corisande Yes. That was what Festus said. Straight forward.

Polly But there be pits and bogs.

Corisande We will avoid them.

Polly And wild beasties. And maybe bogles.

Corisande They'll not harm us if we show no fear.

Polly I'm bound to show fear if there be bogles.

Corisande Why should there be? Come, now we know the right road it can't be far.

Festus is heard singing in the distance again

Polly What about all they nasty Dumps, then? They'll be there for sure. Hundreds of them—like the Witch said.

Corisande We ... we must try not to mind them. (*Leading the way*) The sooner we start the sooner we shall be safe home again.

Polly (*following*) Promise there won't be no bogles?

Corisande Now—what was it Festus said exactly? 'You must go straight forward and alone'. ALONE. I had forgotten that. You need not worry about the bogles Polly. This time I go alone.

Polly Across the moor? Alone?

Corisande That is how it must be. (*She exits*)

Polly (*alone*) What'll I do? What'll I do, then, if harm comes to her? What'll I tell the Queen?

The Princess runs back and clings to Polly

Corisande I can't! I can't! It's so dark and strange. I'm frightened.

Polly There, there, my dearie.

Corisande Come with me, Polly. Come with me. I can't go alone. I can't. . . .

Polly 'Course 'ee can't. Don't tremble so then, dearie. Polly'll come with 'ee.

They start off together hand in hand

Corisande I daresay there won't be any bogles, Polly.

Polly Bogles? Who's a-feared of they?

Again, Festus is heard singing

Corisande No. This is wrong. I must go alone. Goodbye Polly.

Polly But 'ee bain't going all they way alone in the dark!

Corisande Yes. I'm sorry I was so stupid. I'm brave now. Goodbye. Hurry home.

Polly I got to go with 'ee. I got to.

Corisande Not this time.

Polly But I dursn't go back without 'ee. What'll I say?

Corisande Say you obeyed my orders.

Polly Let me come, Mistress. I'll be no trouble.

Corisande It is I who am the trouble. I must go alone or I shall never find my treasure. Don't cry, Polly. I shall come to no harm. There! (*She dries Polly's eyes and kisses her*) Go now. Quickly.

Polly exits, weeping

Corisande Straight forward and alone.

MARGARET GIBBS

THE TREASURE IN THE WITCHBALL

CORISANDE / MARTHA

In this scene Corisande has journeyed alone (although Festus is never too far off) and now finds herself in Old Martha's hut, a wretched place where the only bright thing is a witchball hanging from a beam. Corisande is not a sweet and sugary princess; she has strength and determination. Martha is not a typical 'wicked witch', more of an unpleasant old crone whom life has made bitter

The place is empty when Corisande enters

Corisande What a horrible place—it certainly looks like a Witch's house. Oh! And there's a Witch's broom. Yes, this must be right. Now, if only I can find the Witchball before old Martha ... why, there it is! (*She struggles with the cord that secures it*) Quickly! Quickly! Ah! (*She detaches the ball*) My laugh! My darling laugh! I have you at last!

Martha and her Cat enter

Martha So! The Royal Princess is a thief!

Corisande I take only what is my own. It is my laugh here in this witchball, is it not?

Martha It WAS yours.

Corisande It is mine still. I wish to have it again.

Martha It seems to me there was a bargain made. Something was done and something given in payment. But now, her Royal Highness, keeping still the service, would take the payment back. I am thought an evil thing but this I would not do.

Corisande The bargain was not made by me.

Martha You were a party to it, were you not?

Corisande But I must have my laugh back. I will give you something else instead. Anything. ANYTHING.

Martha You promise rashly. No, Princess, no. What I was asked to do, I did. The price I asked for was paid. Your blemish was removed and I have your laugh. I am content.

Corisande But I am not. I'm young ... so much of life before me. You cannot make me live it always without laughter ... haunted always by these goblin dumps.

Martha And what of me? Am I to be so haunted as before? You think THAT doesn't matter, eh? That Martha ... she's old. Who cares whether the old laugh or cry?

Corisande But after all it is MY laugh. Is it my fault if you've lost your own? Please, please, take my laugh out of the witchball and give it back to me.

Martha Take it out yourself. What stops you?
Corisande I—I do not know how.
Martha Not so easy is it, Your Highness?
Corisande I will have it. I—I will break the ball.
Martha NO! Give it to me!
Corisande So that is the way. How simple!
Martha Break it then. Break the ball and your mother's word and GO.

Princess Corisande again raises the ball, hesitates, then lowers it

Corisande No. I am the Princess Corisande and my word, and my Mother's word stands. Take it quickly . . . (*Martha snatches the ball and goes*)
Corisande (*running to the door*) Open. Open. You SHALL open! (*As she looks round the Dumps are in evidence*) The Dumps again! Oh, so many of them. (*Retreating*) Go away. Go away. Don't touch me! (*She hears singing off stage*) Oh, there's Festus. Festus, Festus! It is I . . . Corisande. Open the door with your lute. What's that you say, Festus? Oh, yes. This is the FOURTH door. (*Remembering*) 'But when you come to the fourth door, then will be needed something more.' What more? What more? What must I do? Oh, these Dumps! If only I could laugh. I must laugh. I WILL laugh. (*She forces a laugh*) Ha . . . ha . . . ha . . . They're drawing back a little I think. Ha, ha . . . ha, ha . . . They look rather silly like that. Yes . . . they do look silly (*She begins to laugh naturally*) They're nothing really. Go along with you, you silly, silly, silly little nothings. (*She laughingly drives the Dumps away*) They're gone! The dumps are all gone!

                                                                          MARGARET GIBBS

VICTORIA BESS

MOGGY / JEMIMA

It is 1879. Two small, ragged girls walk wearily down the London street, the younger dragging tired legs and with one arm in a filthy sling, the older nurses a baby. Both are sickly and starving. At a toy-shop they pause . . .

Moggy (*after a pause during which she gazes at an expensive doll*) Lor! Jemima!

Jemima Ain't she now a perfect lovely . . .

Moggy I never saw anythink like 'er in me life. I 'spose that's 'ow the Princess o' Wales looks when she goes to a ball!

They go on staring at the window

Jemima Do you see 'er little 'ands an' the dimples in 'em? Oh, ain't she a sweet all over? Look, Babsy, look at the beauty, beauty lady. (*She bobs the baby up and down to see*)

Moggy (*keenly*) Wot's she got round 'er neck, Jemima dear?

Jemima Oh, pearls. Them things, you know, that's found at the bottom of the sea, like oysters. Father says they cost a lot of money to buy.

Moggy (*in awe*) What a lot of money she must be worth altogether then. Do you think a pound would buy 'er?

Jemima A pound o' wot? It just all depends on the quality.

Moggy Oh, I don't mean anythink to eat, Jemima. I mean a pound in MONEY.

Jemima Well, a pound MIGHT. A pound's a good bit, ain't it? Yet, I'm sure I don't know. She don't look as if she were meant to be bought do she? Lor! 'Ow I'd like to 'ave 'er out an' give 'er a 'ug.

Moggy (*after a pause, thinking*) Jemima. I've often done things for you 'aven't I?

Jemima Yes. A famous one you've always been gettin' me off with father, when 'e's bin angry, an' standing up fer me. And when I was ill that time in winter with the fever, oh! you was a dear, soothin' me at night, an' speakin' to me as kind as ever mother could. Is there anythink you wants done fer you?

Moggy Yes. Somethink you won't like doing, Jemima, but it'll be over in a minute, an' I does want to know dreadful . . .

Jemima Whatever is it?

Moggy (*a little nervously*) Why, Jemima, it's to go in an' ask what the price of 'er really is. I ain't got the courage to do it meself, but pr'aps, dear, as I've done things for you . . .

Jemima (*rather aghast*) It's such a GRAND shop. The people 'ud certain to be rude and turn me out afore hever they answered me. Look at the great door! look inside! Look at ME! Oh, I COULDN'T!

88

Moggy (*gently*) Very well, Jemima, dear, if you feels as you couldn't, why, I wouldn't press you. (*She feels a twinge of sudden pain in her arm*)
Jemima (*seeing her young sister's face*) Harm 'urt you, Moggy?
Moggy Yes, it's bad this morn. It keeps givin' such sharp shoots, like knives, Jemima.
Jemima (*resolutely; putting the baby on to Moggy's good arm*) I'm a goin' in, Moggy.
Moggy Why, Jemima. Are you . . .? (*But Jemima has gone in*) Lor, Babsy, she's a goin' to ask the price. (*Straining to see*) The lady's lookin' in the glass case. I wonder 'ow much she is Babsy. Ever such a lot, I spects . . .

Jemima returns and takes Baby

Jemima She's three guineas, Moggy. Of course, I know'd she'd be a great price, an' there'd be no good askin'. Whatever did you want so pertickler to know 'er price for?
Moggy Well, Jemima dear, you knows if I 'ave to 'ave me arm off, an' I goes into the 'Ospital. Father says if I goes through it brave an' don't fret, when you comes to see me and leave me on Visitin' Days, that 'e'll buy me a doll; an' I thought—I thought p'raps that I might get 'ER; but of course if she's three guineas. Why, that's more than three sovereigns, ain't it? It's not a bit o' good thinkin' of 'er . . .
Jemima (*decidedly*) No, not a bit. Let's come on now, Moggy dear. It's cold for baby, standin'—ain't it, my beauty bright?
Moggy Well, Jemima, I'm much obliged to you fer goin' in an' askin', 'cos I knows 'ow nasty it was. The woman was a bit short with you, wasn't she? cos you was so quick out.
Jemima She was ever so pertickler, Moggy, case I touched somethink.
Moggy Best not to think of that doll, no more, Jemima . . . too much money for us, she is . . . (*turning for a last look as Jemima, with Baby, moves off*) but, lor—'ow I'd love to 'ave 'er. 'Ow I would. Wait for me, Jemima . . . I'm a-comin' . . .

"BRENDA"

WHEN MARNIE WAS THERE

MARNIE / ANNA

While Anna, often lonely and withdrawn, is recovering from an illness she becomes involved in an unusual friendship with the strangely fascinating Marnie. At this point in the story Anna does not know that Marnie is really the ghost of her own grandmother, as a child. Anna is sitting on the grass when a rustle tells her that Marnie is there. Place: Norfolk. Time: now

Marnie (*laughing*) You do look a solemn goose, staring like that. What are you looking for, mushrooms in the sky?

Anna (*amazed*) Goodness! However did you get here? You're almost magic!

Marnie Come on, slowcoach, mushrooms.

Marnie takes Anna's hand and runs with her to the mushrooms. They start to fill the bags Anna has with her

Anna How on earth did you know exactly where to go each time? I couldn't even see those little button ones till we were right on top of them.

Marnie Well, I ought to know the best places by now. I've been here long enough.

Anna You are lucky. (*Enviously*) How long?

Marnie Every summer of my life—as long as I can remember. What are you looking so gloomy about, all of a sudden? Come down here, out of the wind.

Anna You are lucky. I wish I was you.

Marnie Why?

Anna Because—you're—oh, nothing . . . (*She gloomily chews grass*)

Marnie Tell me now who wanted to get rid of you and why. Don't your parents love you?

Anna I haven't any parents. I'm well, sort of adopted. I live with Mr and Mrs Preston. They're called Auntie and Uncle, but they're not really.

Marnie Oh, poor you! (*Almost as if she hoped so*) Are they cruel to you?

Anna No, they're very kind to me. At least, she is. I don't see him very much, he's always busy, but I think he's kind too. He's quite nice.

Marnie But what happened to your real parents?

Anna My father went away—I don't know where—and my mother married someone else . . . (*Anna uses a monotonous little tone here*) and then they went away on a holiday—and I was staying with my granny—and they got killed in a car accident.

Marnie Oh, POOR you! How dreadful for you. Did you go into mourning? Did you mind terribly?

90

Anna No, I didn't mind at all. I don't even remember it. I told you, I was living with my granny . . .

Marnie Go on.

Anna (*flatly*) Well, then she died.

Marnie Oh, but why?

Anna (*shrugging*) How should I know? She went away to some place because she said she wasn't very well, and she promised to come back soon, but she didn't. She died instead, at least that's what Miss Hannay said.

Marnie Who's Miss Hannay?

Anna A lady who comes to see me sometimes. At least, she comes to see Mrs Preston and talk about me. It's her job, you see, to go and see children who're sort of adopted like I am. She has to see me too, and she asks about school and things. She's quite nice, but I never know what to say to her. I did ask her once about Granny—because I sort of remembered her—and she said she'd died. (*Defiantly*) So what! Who cares?

Marnie (*shocked*) But didn't you love her?

Anna (*after a pause, sullenly*) No, I hate her. And I hate my mother. I hate them all. That's the thing . . .

Marnie (*puzzled*) But your mother couldn't HELP being killed?

Anna She left me before she was killed, to go away on holiday.

Marnie (*reasonably*) And your granny couldn't help dying.

Anna She left me too. She went away. And she promised to come back and she didn't. (*Angrily*) I hate her for leaving me all alone, and not staying to look after me. It wasn't fair of her to leave me . . . I'll never forgive her. I hate her.

Marnie (*comforting her*) In a way I think you're lucky to be sort of adopted. I've often thought, secretly, that I'm adopted—don't tell, will you?—and in a way I wish I was. That would prove how terribly kind my mother and father are, to have adopted me when I was a poor little orphan baby with no-one to look after me.

Anna I should have thought anyone would rather have their own mother and father—if they knew them . . . (*Looking thoughtfully at Marnie*) If I tell you a deep secret will you promise never to tell?

Marnie Of course! We're telling secrets all the time, aren't we? I wouldn't DREAM of telling.

Anna Well, it's about Mr and Mrs Preston. I told you they're kind to me and they are, but I thought they looked after me and everything because they . . . well, because I was like their own child, but I found out a little while ago—(*Whispering*)—they're paid to do it.

Marnie (*eyes widening*) Oh, no! Are you sure? How do you know?

Anna I found a letter. It was in the sideboard drawer. It was a printed letter and it was something about how the council was going to increase the allowance for me, and there was a cheque inside as well.

Marnie Oh! Whatever did you do?

Anna When she came home I tried to ask her about it. I couldn't say I'd read the letter, at least I didn't want to. Anyway I wanted to ask her first. So I said didn't it cost an awful lot to feed me and hadn't my new winter coat cost a lot, and things like that. And all she said was that they liked to do it, and I wasn't to worry, and if it was because I'd heard her saying they were hard up I wasn't to take it seriously. Everyone said they were hard up and it didn't mean anything. So I kept on asking questions about money and how much things cost, and things like that. I tried and tried. I gave her every chance I could to tell me. But she wouldn't. She just kept on saying she loved me and I wasn't to worry. Then afterwards—I went to look—the letter had gone. She'd hidden it. So then I knew it was true.

Marnie (*thinking*) DOES that mean she doesn't love you, though?

Anna (*trying to be fair*) I think in a way she does, sort of. But you can see the difference, can't you? How would you like to have someone PAID to love you? Anyway, after that, I think she guessed that I knew. She kept looking at me as if she was worried, and wanting to know why I was always asking questions about money. And she kept trying to do things to please me. But it wasn't the same then—it couldn't be.

Marnie Why don't you ask Miss Hannay?

Anna (*shocked*) Oh, no. That would be mean. Anyway I couldn't talk to her about it, I hardly know her. She knows all about me, but I don't know anything about her, not really. It would have been mean to ask her behind their backs. Anyway I knew already. I didn't need her to tell me what I'd found out for myself. But (*Beginning to cry*) . . . I do so wish she'd told me herself. I gave her such a lot of chances.

Marnie Dear Anna, I love you. I love you more than any girl I've ever known. There! Does that make you feel better?

Anna smiles at Marnie, as if a weight is lifted from her

Adapted from the novel by
JOAN ROBINSON

THE WITCH'S DAUGHTER

JANEY / PERDITA

Janey, an eleven-year-old blind girl is playing alone on the beach while her brother, Tim, explores a large rock some way off. The strange girl, Perdita, has been watching her from the sand dunes, and gradually comes closer

Janey (*singing to herself for a while as she decorates the sand with shells. She then realizes that Perdita is close*) I thought you'd come.

Perdita moves in even closer, so that Janey may touch her skirt

Go on. Say something . . . You CAN talk, can't you?

Perdita nods

Are you dumb?

She tugs at Perdita's skirt

Perdita (*softly*) No. (*She moves away a little; nervously*)
Janey (*sensing this*) What's your name? (*Coaxing*) Please—won't you tell me your name?
Perdita (*with a small gasp*) Perdita . . .
Janey That's pretty. How do you spell it?
Perdita I—I—don't know.
Janey Don't know?
Perdita I can't . . . (*On an impulse*) Can you read and write? Can you teach me?
Janey (*slowly*) Braille. I can do braille. But that's not . . .
Perdita LETTERS. (*Shivering with eagerness*) Can you show me letters? (*She thrusts a flat shell into Janey's hand*) Look—write in the sand. Write my name.
Janey (*hesitating*) I'm not very good at ordinary letters. I mean, I know the shape, but writing's hard. You can't feel what you've done.
Perdita You can feel in the sand. Please, Janey.
Janey (*putting down the shell*) I can do it best with my finger, I think. (*Slowly, carefully, she draws a letter P in the sand*)
Perdita What's that?
Janey P. That's P for Perdita.
Perdita (*laughing*) Let me. (*She copies it several times*) Now YOUR name.
Janey J. J is for Janey. And for Jam. And A is for Apple. That's how you learn. (*She writes the whole name*)
Perdita (*repeating*) J is for Janey . . . and Jam. . . . A is for Apple.
Janey N is for Nuts.
Perdita N is for Nuts.
Janey E is for Egg.

93

Perdita E is for Egg.

Janey Don't you go to school?

Perdita No. They won't let me.

Janey They? Who are THEY, Perdita? Why won't they let you go to school?

Perdita Oh, Mr Smith thinks I'll carry tales. He likes to be private ... Please, Janey—oh, please write some more. Write me your brother's name.

Janey T ... T is for Tomato ... I for Ink ... M for Mother ... TIM.

Perdita Tim ... Tim ... TIM ... (*Excited, as she realizes how the letters make the word*) TIM ... TIM ...

Janey (*who thinks she is calling Tim*) Is Tim coming back already? He said he was going exploring on the big rock? Can you see him, Perdita?

Perdita (*looking and suddenly feeling cold, trembling*) I can't exactly see him. He's hurt. I can feel that he's hurt.

Janey Perdita! Are you sure? How? How do you know?

Perdita I just know. I get this feeling. Annie says it's the Second Sight. She says I've got the Second Sight because I'm a Witch's Daughter ...

Janey Tim ...

Adapted from the novel by
NINA BAWDEN

ALAN AND THE KING'S DAUGHTERS

ALAN / WINNIE

Based on the story of the Twelve Dancing Princesses. Alan, a young wood-cutter, in love with Susanna, the youngest princess, is here disguised and masked in an effort to outwit Winnie the Witch. You will have to imagine the Cat unless you are allowed to use an "extra"

Alan and the Cat enter. Alan wears a mask

Alan Madam, I, the Great Panjandrum, challenge you forthwith to the Contest of Supernatural Strength.

Winnie What's that? The Contest of Supernatural Strength? All three rounds.

Alan All three rounds. Riddles, then the Summoning up of Spirits and the Great Ruling.

Winnie Indeed. You must think you are a magician of quite considerable powers if you are prepared to try the Great Ruling against me. You do know who I am?

Alan You are a witch, madam.

Winnie Not an ordinary witch. A witch of great renown. You realize that failure in the Great Ruling means death?

Alan I do realize it. But to save these fair ladies and their noble father, I am willing to risk my life.

Winnie Enough of this talking. Shall we begin—or have you lost heart already?

Alan I am ready to begin, Madam Witch.

Winnie Let the Contest of Supernatural Strength begin!

Alan and Winnie face each other diagonally. A minor chord sounds before each riddle. After each answer is accepted they move anti-clockwise, along the sides of an invisible square

Winnie (*chanted, not sung*)
        Answer my riddle, answer my rhyme.
        Answer me now till the end of time.
        It's dark in the country, it's dark in the town.
        When darkness comes fleeting, it swallows it down.
        It's here and it's there, and it's always behind.
        It follows you always. It's ticklish to find.

Alan I know! Your shadow!

Winnie Correct, my Great Panjandrum. Correct. Now it is your turn.

Alan Answer my riddle, answer my rhyme.
        Answer me now till the end of time.
        It comes from the lips, yet it makes not a sound
        It's welcome at all times; it appears all around.

One given brings another, it makes dark days bright
You've seen it, you've given it—now tell it aright.

Winnie Sentimental tosh! It's a smile, of course. Tho' smiles will not get
you very far today. What about this?

A woeful face to hide what you would hide.
A pleasant surface o'er what lurks inside.

Alan "O'er what lurks inside," Lurks—yet a *pleasant* face. It must be a
mask of some sort—no. I cannot guess.

Winnie A lie, a lie! A very useful little concealment. Now if I guess your
second riddle you've lost.

Alan In all the world the brightest light.
It scorns even the darkest night.

Winnie The moon? No. It's often behind the clouds. The sun? It doesn't
shine at night. I must admit you have me baffled!

Alan The truth.

Winnie (*shaken*) I see. I see. That round is over; we both qualify. The
truth—ugh!

Alan Yes. The truth. It is a powerful weapon against the powers of
darkness.

Winnie You're wasting time. What about the summoning up of a spirit;
eh? Shall I go first?

Alan bows. Winnie invokes a fearsome evil spirit

*Alan, obviously very worried, makes a few vaguely incantory gestures,
invoking the Cat*

*The Cat, draped in a white sheet, enters and does a dance to comic music
Winnie catches sight of the Cat's tail, which now has its own white tip. She
whips off the sheet*

Winnie You call this a spirit. It's that wicked animal who refused to
become my familiar. And what's this. A white tip to your tail! You
deceived me! Only the hairs from a jet black cat will make my spell
work. You spoiled my magic. You caused all this trouble. But you'll
cause no more trouble—not as long as I've some power left—and I've
plenty of that.

Wicked creature, lie there,
Never more to rise.
Be as dead until the hour
That I give up my magic power—
And I'll *never* give up my power. (*She laughs*)

*The Cat slowly sinks to the ground and is still. Alan takes off his mask and
kneels down beside him*

Alan Cat! Cat! You mustn't die now. (*To the Witch*) You heartless,
monstrous fiend—how could you do that?

Winnie So—it's the bold Alan, is it? Everything is falling into place. One
more round, and I'll settle you as well.

Alan I don't think I can go on—but I *must*. I can't give in, even though I
know I'll lose, even though Cat . . .

Winnie Now for the Great Ruling. I am the most powerful witch in the whole world—*and* the cleverest. I can make anyone do what I want. Just look what I did to Cat! I can make—to take the first example that springs to mind—all these children do what I want. Nasty children they are, too. Interfering. Helping Alan and Cat. I can ask them to do something for me. And they will. They must! Now let me think. (*She goes up stage*)

Alan (*to the audience*) Children—please! Don't be afraid. Perhaps we've still a chance to break her power and save Cat. Whatever she asks, try your best to refuse.

Winnie (*returning*) Children, I command you—by all the ancient tradition of the Great Ruling—*Stand*. Did you hear? I command you to *Stand*. What! You must! Won't you—oh, it kills me to say it—*please* stand? Wretches. Miserable little wretches, not to do as I say . . .

Alan Excuse me. It's my turn now. Children, for me, for truth, for the Princess—for Cat—children—will you stand up for *Cat*?

The children stand

Winnie Finished! Finished! My powers are gone. I must dwell for ever in the depths of all dark despair . . .

Winnie exits wailing

The Cat begins to stir

Alan Look! He's getting better—thanks to *you.*

The Cat recovers and shakes hands with the audience

HELEN MURDOCH

BLEAK HOUSE

JO / LADY

This Dickens novel is full of plots, sub-plots and fascinating characters. Mixed up in one part of the tale is Jo, the little crossing sweeper, poor and ragged. He does not realize his involvement and in one of his favourite sayings insists "I don't know nothink". A handsome and rich lady needs information, and he finds he can assist her. She is Lady Dedlock . . . elegant, attractive, though past her early youth. Set in Victorian London, near the Inns of Court, as well as in a seedier area. You will have to stage the scene with care to make the distances seem right

Lady Are you the boy I've read of in the papers?

Jo I don't know. I don't know nothink about nothink at all.

Lady Were you examined at an Inquest?

Jo I don't know nothink about noth . . . where I was took by the beadle, d'you mean? Was the boy's name at the Inkwhich, JO?

Lady Yes.

Jo That's me.

Lady Come farther up.

Jo (*following her*) You mean about the man? Him as wos dead?

Lady Hush. Speak in a whisper. Yes. Did he look, when he was living, so very ill and poor?

Jo O jist.

Lady (*with abhorrence*) Did he look like—not like YOU?

Jo O, not so bad as me. I'm a reg'lar one, I am. You didn't know him, did you?

Lady How dare you ask me if I knew him?

Jo (*with much humility*) No offence, my lady . . .

Lady I am not a lady. I am . . . a . . . a servant.

Jo (*admiringly*) You are a jolly servant.

Lady Listen and be silent. Don't talk to me, and stand farther from me. Can you show me all those places that were spoken of in the account I read? The place he wrote for, the place he died at, the place where you were taken to, and the place where he was buried? Do you know the place where he was buried?

Jo nods at each question

Go before me, and show me all those dreadful places. Stop opposite to each and do not speak to me unless I speak to you. Don't look back. Do what I want and I will pay you well.

As she speaks Jo counts off the words on his broom handle, nodding

Jo I'm fly. But fen larks, you know. Stow hooking it.

Lady What does the horrible creature mean?
Jo Stow cutting away, you know.
Lady I don't understand you. Go on before. I will give you more money
than you ever had in your life.

Jo leads the way . . . then stops. A pause

Who lives here?
Jo Him wot give him his writing an' give me half a bull.
Lady Go on to the next.

Jo leads on . . . stops again. Longer pause

Who lives here?
Jo HE lived here.
Lady (*after a pause*) In which room?
Jo In the back room up there. You can see the winder from this corner.
Up there . . . That's where I see 'im stritched out.
Lady Go on to the next . . .

Jo leads her to an iron gate, in a filthy court-yard

Jo He was put there.
Lady Where? O, what a scene of horror.
Jo There. Over yonder. Among them piles of bones an' close to that there
kitchin winder. They put him wery nigh the top. They was obliged to
stamp upon it to get it in. I could uncover it for you with my broom if
the gate was open. That's why they locks it I suppose. It's always
locked. Look at the rat. Hi. Look. . . . There he goes. . . . Ho . . . into
the ground . . .
Lady (*shrinking away in loathing*) Is this place of abomination consecrated
ground?
Jo I don't know nothink of consequential ground.
Lady Is it blessed?
Jo Which?
Lady Is it blessed?
Jo I'm blest if I know, but I shouldn't think it warn't. Blest? It ain't done
it much good if it is. Blest? I should think it was the other meself. But I
don't know nothink.
Lady (*handing him money, taking care not to touch him*) Now, show me the
spot again.
Jo (*pushing his broom through the gate*) There. They put him near the top.
He give me money for me supper and lodging. He never had no friends
neither like me. He wos very good ter me. When I see him lying stritched
out I wished he could have heard me tell him so.

The Lady has gone, quietly away

Cor . . . she's gone.

*He runs to the light to look at the coin. Then bites it to make sure. He looks
around*

He wos very good ter me, he wos.

Putting the coin in his mouth for safety, he goes off sweeping

Adapted from the novel by
CHARLES DICKENS

THE CAR

PIP / LUKE

Luke, fifteen, has run away from foster parents and has been sleeping rough in an old car. A gang of boys and girls befriend him, and he finds he is able to talk to Pip, a girl of about thirteen

Time: the present

Luke shouts with pain and wriggles out. He has cut his arm. He gets up, holding the wounded arm carefully. Pip has kept behind him so that he does not know she is there

Pip Let me help. Have you hurt yourself?
Luke (*turning and seeing her*) Oh, hello. Didn't know you were there. Not much. Just cut it on a bit of metal.

Pip inspects the wound, opens her bag, takes out a handkerchief for a piece of cloth

Pip Sit up there.

Luke sits on the car bonnet. Pip begins to doctor the wound

Pip It's not too bad. Soon have it O.K. Men always shout before they're hurt. I've brought you some dinner.
Luke Thanks. (*He winces*) Ow!
Pip Stop bellowing. Anyone would think you were dying.
Luke Girls are hard.
Pip Nonsense. I've got your clothes too.
Luke Do I *have* to change?
Pip Of course. Can't keep you with us if you don't look normal like the rest of us. Somebody is bound to ask questions if the council men do come. And anyway, I've told my mum I've a friend I want to bring home, so you'd better look right!
Luke Bossy as well as hard, girls are.
Pip Why? Don't you want to come?
Luke Yes. Wouldn't mind. You're O.K., you lot.
Pip (*finishing the dressing*) Thanks, kind sir! Anyway, you'll have to change. You smell as you are.
Luke Huh! (*He laughs. An idea occurs to him. He reseats himself primly on the bonnet and gives Pip a huge, toothy smile. He imitates a TV advert voice*) Even your best friends won't tell you. Beware! You can have it without knowing. (*He holds out his arms languidly, sniffs under his armpits, blows out and pulls a disgusted face*) Don't be rank, rancid or tainted; musty, fusty or frousty. (*He gives the toothy grin*) Use "Honesty" —the soap that blows away the B.O. in big bouncy bubbles. Don't just

be clean—(*He smells under his arms again, but this time returns an exotic look*)—*smell* clean, with fragrant "Honesty".

Pip (*laughing*) I've thought of that too.

Luke Oh, no!

Pip (*taking soap and a towel from her bag*) Here's some soap, and a towel. There's a pool over there. You can clean up in a minute.

Luke Is there anything you haven't thought of?

Pip Yes—a toothbrush. So you'll have to finish off with this apple. (*She takes an apple from her bag*)

Luke (*taking the apple and getting down from the bonnet*) Thanks. And thanks for doing up my arm.

Pip That's all right.

A pause. Luke is gnawing the apple

You know I really am surprised your mum lets you roam about like you do. Ours wouldn't let us.

Luke is arrested as he is about to take a bite of the apple. His hand drops to his side. He breathes in deeply

Luke (*with difficulty*) I haven't got a mother.

Pip is taken aback

Pip Oh. . . . I'm sorry, Luke . . . I didn't know.

Luke It's O.K. Don't worry. It's over. Nothing to bother about. (*He gets into the car*) Where's them clothes?

Pip But, Luke . . . if you've no mother then . . .

Luke Girls are nosey too! Ask no questions and you'll get no lies. One day you'll know maybe. I'll tell you. But not yet. It's all over. See?

Pip If it was all over you wouldn't be here, would you?

Luke (*uncertainly*) How d'you mean?

Pip Stands to reason. If it was all over, you'd be settled somewhere. You should be in school or at work and you're not.

Luke Proper old Sherlock Holmes, ain't you!

Pip That's what Eddie said, and he was right.

Luke Been talking about me, have you?

Pip I told you last night it was odd finding you here like we did. We're bound to wonder, aren't we? Luke . . . it's not that I'm nosey or any-thing . . . just, it would be nice to know about you. We all like you.

Luke I know. It's been good these last two days. At first I liked it up here 'cos it was out of the way and nobody came. I'd been on the road nearly five days then, and I was just beginning to feel like going back.

Pip Back where, Luke?

Luke Back to the woman who looks after me. Lovejoy her name is. Mrs Lovejoy. Her husband's dead and they didn't have any kids. She got me after . . . after mum and dad went.

Pip Do you like her?

Luke Mrs Lovejoy? She's O.K. She always done her best for me. She's kind and all that, you know. I'm fond of her really. But . . . somehow . . . it isn't enough. I get restless. Once before I ran off. Tramped about for eight days that time. Copper in Huddersfield picked me up. Ever been to Huddersfield?

Pip No.

Luke Then don't. Not even if you want to go somewhere no-one will think of looking! Anyhow, yesterday I was in half a mind to go back and just hope that she hadn't asked the coppers to look for me again—I'd really get it this time, if she did.

Pip But you didn't.

Luke No. You lot came. And it's been different since. Like a different world, where it didn't matter who I was or what had happened to me. You all just took me as I am.

He pauses. They look at each other. Then with a great breath, he makes himself active again

As I say, it's been great with you lot—and now I'm going to change ready for the rest of the fun. (*He gets out of the car, takes the bag and is about to exit, when he stops and turns back slowly, a wry smile on his face*) Here! No looking, mind!

Pip (*laughing*) I won't. I promise. Anyway—doubt if you're any different from our Paul.

Luke No. Except Paul's your brother, isn't he?

Pip (*more cautiously*) Yes, he is.

Luke And that makes a difference, don't it?

Pip Yes, I suppose it does.

Luke Yeah! Well . . . see you!

He turns to go off

AIDAN CHAMBERS

CHRISTMAS IN THE MARKET PLACE

MARY / ANGEL

This play was written in 1935 for a small amateur group in France. A family of strolling gypsy players put on a play one Christmas, in the market place. In this scene the daughter-in-law, Maria, takes the part of Mary and Bruno, the grandson acts out the Angel. There is a simplicity in this writing which needs to be echoed in the playing

The Angel, who is Bruno, approaches downstage, carrying a basket of flowers, in which a dove is supposed to be sleeping

Angel (*to himself and to the public*) Yes, this is it! I nearly went in the wrong door. I am a little absent-minded—it's emotion. (*Stopping*) Oh! My heart is beating like a bird you hold in your hand—like the dove in my basket . . . (*He strokes the dove*) Sweet! Sweet! She's sleeping among the flowers . . . (*A pause*) It is the first time the Heavenly Father has given me a job of this sort. Carry to a young girl—to a completely pure young girl, the purest of all—she was created for this—the news that she will be a mother—that she will bear a little boy. Without marriage. Without a lover. And this tiny creature will be God. No more, no less—God! But flesh and blood, like a little man. What a mystery! What a mystery! Although I'm an angel—and one of the more intelligent angels—oh! I am not boasting about it—God made me an angel, an archangel, a super-angel!—Well, all the same, I can't understand it. The Heavenly Father is cleverer than I am. It is His business.

A pause. He takes a step to mount the platform

She does not move. She does not realize. She is listening to that fat blackbird singing among the leaves. He sways the branch, shaking the tiny stars of jasmine. The jasmine smells sweet. See how she breathes the scent, scarcely widening her nostrils. (*A pause*) There she is: waiting. The world is so lovely to her that she waits for its salvation. He who made it lovely shall save it. But how can she dream that she could help him in the saving? She thinks herself insignificant among created things. What use would she be to Him? God does not need men: it is men who need God. (*He mounts the platform*) Shall I warn her, or take her by surprise? I might cough or sing . . . (*He coughs gently*) Hum! . . . Hum! Hum! . . . No, she does not hear. I will stand under the jasmine, play my flute, and wait till she sees me.

He moves to stand opposite Mary and plays several notes: 'Ave, ave, ave Maria'. A pause

Mary What a lovely song! Oh! the perfume! The light! (*She sees the Angel*) Ah! someone is there! (*She rises*)
Angel Hail, Mary, full of grace . . .

Mary (*aside*) How did he get in? Who is he?

Angel The Lord is with thee.

Mary (*softly*) With me?

Angel Blessed art thou among women. (*He comes nearer and salutes again*)

Mary He is beautiful! And he greets me! He is not made of flesh—that is impossible. (*A pause*) Am I dreaming?—No, I am not dreaming. He comes near. (*She recoils a little*) Why does he salute me? I am ashamed. (*A pause*) I am frightened.

Angel Fear not, Mary . . . (*moved*) for . . . for . . . thou hast found favour . . . with God. (*Aside*) This is the moment to tell her— Courage! I dare not! Little dove, help me. (*Aloud*) Behold, thou shalt conceive in thy womb—and bring forth a child, Mary—a son—and shalt call His name Jesus. He shall be great, and shall be called the Son of the Highest: and the Lord God shall give unto Him the throne of His father David: and He shall reign over the house of Jacob for ever—and of His kingdom there shall be no end.

Mary (*Softly*) There shall be no end. (*Aloud*) I do not understand—I am amazed—and do not understand. May I sit down?—I am trembling. But is it for fear or happiness? (*Softly*) The Messiah . . . the Messiah . . . in me? (*A pause*) How shall this be—seeing I know not a man?

Angel (*taking the imaginary dove in his hand*) The Holy Ghost shall come upon thee, and the power of the Highest shall overshadow thee. (*He raises the dove above Mary*) Therefore also that Holy Thing which shall be born of thee shall be called the Son of God. And, behold, thy cousin Elisabeth, she hath also conceived a son in her old age: and this is the sixth month with her, who was called barren. For with God nothing shall be impossible.

A pause. Mary slowly bows down.

What reply shall I give Him, Mary?

Mary (*prostrating herself*) Behold the handmaid of the Lord. Be it unto me according to thy word.

Angel (*releasing the dove*) See! The dove has flown! To God! . . . The Lord is with you, Mary. I leave you my basket of flowers.

He puts down the basket in front of her, and goes out gently. A pause. Mary lifts her head

Mary He has gone. But I am not alone . . . I shall never be alone again, O God. For I carry in my womb the predestined, the elect, the King— Christ, the ransom of earthly sin. (*Seeing the basket*) He has left his flowers. (*Taking, and looking at them*) They smell of Paradise. White roses . . . white roses . . . so many white roses. Ah! One red rose—red as blood! (*She pricks herself*) Ah! it pricks . . . I pricked my finger— and my blood stains the flower. The white ones are lovely. But I prefer the red . . . although it pricked me.

She holds it in her hand, rises, carrying the basket in the other hand, and goes out smelling it

A child—from God. A child—from God.

She goes out　　　　　　　　　　　　　　　　　　HENRI GHEON

THE DOLLS HOUSE

MARCHPANE / MR PLANTAGENET

A group of dolls who include Mr Plantagenet and his wife Birdie have lived a long time in Charlotte and Emily's dolls house. Now a valuable—and very conceited and elegant—doll, Marchpane, has been put in the house too. In this scene she and Mr Plantagenet are on the sofa. He stares hard at her. (Marchpane is a heavy, sweet, sickly stuff like almond icing, very old-fashioned. You very quickly have enough of it. This gives a clue to March-pane's character)

Marchpane (*sharply*) Don't do that.

Mr Plantagenet Don't do what?

Marchpane Stare and stare and stare. It's very rude.

Mr. Plantagenet (*politely*) I am sorry. But I can't help staring.

Marchpane I suppose they are fixed.

Mr Plantagenet Fixed?

Marchpane They don't open and shut?

Mr Plantagenet Open and shut?

Marchpane Your eyes. Take them off me at once.

Mr Plantagenet (*still more politely*) Excuse me. My eyes are not on you. They are in me.

Marchpane Faugh! You should be in the hall, not sitting in a chair. If you sit at all, it should be in the kitchen.

Mr Plantagenet (*bewildered*) Excuse me. Why should I be in the hall and the kitchen? Why shouldn't I sit? I'm jointed.

Marchpane Are you not the butler? There used to be a butler, I'm sure.

Mr Plantagenet (*correcting her*) The figure of a butler. He is gone to dust. I don't know what a butler is. But I do know I am not one. I am a post-master and besides, I am the master of this house. Do you know that carol? 'God bless the master of this house, God bless the Mistress too?' Well, I am the master and Birdie is the Mistress.

Marchpane That she certainly is not.

Mr Plantagenet (*positively*) Oh yes, she is.

Marchpane She isn't. I am.

Mr Plantagenet You? Oh no! How could you be? I have never seen you before and I have seen Birdie. Do you know who I thought you were? I thought you might be the Fairy off the Christmas tree. Birdie is always talking about her. Are you the fairy off the Christmas tree?

Marchpane A fairy? I am real. Far more real than Birdie.

Mr Plantagenet (*anxiously*) Does Birdie know that?

There is a bumping sound on the other side of the wall

Marchpane What is that?

106

Mr Plantagenet That is Apple.

Marchpane Apple?

Mr Plantagenet The little boy doll. Our little boy. He belongs to us.

Marchpane (*thoughtfully*) Does he? What is that rustling sound upstairs?

Mr Plantagenet That is Birdie.

Marchpane It is too light to be anyone.

Mr Plantagenet Birdie is light.

Marchpane I am heavy. (*Listening*) What is she doing?

Mr Plantagenet I expect she is dusting the paper chain with her feather broom.

Marchpane Paper chains? With a feather broom? What a very odd thing to do. What did you say her name was?

Mr Plantagenet Birdie.

Marchpane It does sound like a bird rustling. It's an aggravating noise.

Mr Plantagenet I like to hear her . . . she IS like a small bird . . . one that goes for short flights, and collects bits of things to make her nest.

Marchpane I wish you would stop her.

Mr Plantagenet Oh, no. I shouldn't like to disturb her.

Marchpane I shall disturb her!

Mr Plantagenet But . . . you wouldn't! You couldn't.

Marchpane Why not?

Mr Plantagenet It . . . it is cruel to disturb a bird in its nest.

Marchpane Faugh! (*Her eyes seem to glare at him*) I do wish Emily and Charlottle or whatever their names are would come and put me in my own room.

Mr Plantagenet (*thinking anxiously*) Excuse me . . . but . . . er . . . which is your room?

Marchpane (*smartly*) The one with the pink carpet of course.

Mr Plantagenet But that is Birdie's. She chose it. That is Birdie's nest . . . bed . . . room.

Marchpane If you really want to know the whole house is mine.

Mr Plantagenet Wh-a-t? But it's our house. Ours. That we dreamed of . . . that we wanted . . . that we wished for . . .

Marchpane (*yawning*) I can't help what you did for it. It is mine. Mine . . . and really . . . (*yawning again*) I can't live in it with all these people, bumping and rustling and having silly ideas that it is theirs. I must tell Emily and Charlotte.

Mr Plantagenet But . . . you don't understand. This is our house. It is full of us. It was for us. We were on the hearthrug when the letter came. We saw Emily and Charlotte clean it and make it new again and we helped them by wishing. We wished so hard . . . you don't know. We waited for the curtains and the blankets on the beds, and the couch and chairs. You don't know. Now I shall go every day to the Post Office and come back again . . . And this Christmas was so beautiful. You don't know . . . Oh truly, truly, you don't know.

Marchpane What you don't know, and had better know, is that I was here, here in this dolls' house, long, long years ago. Long, long before any of you.

Mr Plantagenet (*firmly*) Not before Tottie you weren't. Tottie has been

here as long as you have. Why, she remembers your coming, she has
been here longer.

Marchpane Tottie! A farthing doll!

Mr Plantagenet A farthing, or a penny, or a sixpence or a pound, she has
been here longer. Tottie is Tottie. She always is and she always has been.
Tottie! Tottie! TOTTIE!

RUMER GODDEN

FAT KING MELON

PRINCESS / KING

Written specially to be acted at Barbara Wadsworth's 10th birthday party,

November 25th, 1924. The king and Princess Caraway have met and fallen in love before this scene takes place, but both were in disguise at the time. He was once VERY fat as the title suggests. The little song at the end is meant to be sung by the Fairy Mumbo, but it could be spoken (or sung) by Caraway and Melon, to complete the scene

Left to herself, the Princess tip-toes guiltily to a secret drawer, from which she takes a large and familiar purple handkerchief

The Princess (*pressing the handkerchief to her lips*) Ah, would that my dear fat husbandman were coming to see me, instead of this ridiculous King! (*Sighing*) I will sing a sad song about Love.
> *Air*, "Barbara Allen"
> Oh, dear! Oh, dear! Oh, dear! Oh, dear!
> Oh, dear! Oh, dear! Oh, de-ar!
> Oh, dear! Oh, dear! Oh, dear! Oh, dear!
> Oh, dear! Oh, dear! Oh, de-ar!

While she is again pressing the handkerchief to her lips, the door opens

The King is now in his crown and robes, but, doubtless as a result of his recent exertions, he has become extraordinarily thin

The King (*bowing low*) Your Highness!
The Princess (*curtseying*) Your Majesty!

Music: Stately Dance

The King (*aside*) Charming! But how horribly fat!
The Princess (*aside*) Goodness! What a scarecrow!—Won't you sit down?

They sit down, side by side

The King (*heavily*) Your Highness, I have come to make a formal request for your hand in marriage. (*Surveying again the monstrous form beside him; with disgust, aside*) Pouf! This is impossible! To think that I was once as fat myself!
The Princess (*with her woman's intuition—aside*). The pig! he does not like me!
The King But I am a kind man, and after all these years I should not wish you to feel bound to me by your plighted word, if you were not willing.

109

The Princess (*haughtily*) It is evident that His Majesty no longer desires the marriage; in which case the Princess is very ready to release him.

The King (*anxiously*) Pray do not misunderstand me. (*At this point his features are suddenly contracted into a frightful expression of pain and apprehension—and after a moment's struggle he cries*) I am going to sneeze. Quick! A handkerchief!

The Princess, after a little fumbling, nobly produces and hands to him the romantic purple handkerchief. But the King is so surprised to see this that he no longer wants to sneeze

The King (*to himself—examining the handkerchief*) Strange! Yes. These are the Royal Initials! (*To the Princess—laughing*) It is a curious coincidence, Your Highness, but this is mine! Ha!—Some mistake at the laundry, I dare say.

The Princess (*startled, peers into his face, places her hands on her heart and remarks, aside*) Gracious! Can it be my husbandman? (*She takes another look*) It is. And he doesn't like me any more! (*She begins to cry and holds out her hand for the handkerchief*)

The King (*embarrassed—rises*) Pardon me, Your Highness, it has naturally given you pain to bring to an end our long and honourable betrothal. But, believe me, I bear you no ill-will for the decision you have made— none whatever. Consider yourself at liberty. And now I will take my leave. (*Bowing*) Your Highness, good day! (*He turns and walks away with dignity*)

At the door, however, a thought strikes him and he returns, stands by the weeping woman and holds out his hand. She stops weeping and looks up at him

The King Pardon me. I think you have my handkerchief.

The Princess (*sadly—giving it to him*) Have you forgotten the little sempstress to whom you gave this token?

The King (*warmly*) On the contrary—she is ever in my thoughts!

The Princess (*brokenly—fixing her eyes on his*) You *have* forgotten her!

The King (*starting*) What! Can it be? But no! For she was as slender as a larch, and you, Princess, if you will forgive my saying so, are not. Alas, I shall never be happy with a fat woman again.

The Princess (*doing something to her dress*) I don't know if it will make any difference, Your Majesty, but, the truth is, I have got a pillow in my bozzom. (*And, sure enough, she extracts from her bosom a huge pillow and other padding, and immediately becomes thin again*)

The King (*delighted and amazed—embraces her*) My Queen! My Caraway!

The Princess You see, dear Melon, I wanted to be fat for your sake, but try as I would, I could not put on flesh. So I thought I would pretend.

The King Ha! And I have well-nigh killed myself with trying to be thin for your sake. Well, well, this will be a lesson to both of us.

The Princess It will be a lesson to me not to consult that quack of a Fairy again.—Oo.

Enter the Fairy Mumbo

Fairy Mumbo (*sententiously*)
>   *Air,* "My Lady Wind"
>   This lesson all around we see;
>   The rabbits wish they were not wee;
>   The elephants would like to be
>   As tiny as the elves;
>   But wishing never swelled a chest,
>   Don't think at all about the rest;
>   Whate'er you be, to be the best,
>   Be first of all yourselves.

The King Cease this offensive moralizing, and let us have a dance!

A. P. HERBERT

FLAMBARDS

CHRISTINA / WILLIAM

This scene comes from the first book of the trilogy. Christina, 12 and an orphan, has come to live at Flambards, a country house, with her Uncle Russell and his sons Mark and Will. The time is 1908. The scene takes place at night. William has broken his leg, and is meant to be resting it. Christina hears a noise and comes to investigate. When she opens his door she is apalled to see him standing, quite unsupported, an agonized look on his face

Christina WILLIAM! (*She shuts the door*) Whatever are you doing? Are you mad? (*She puts her candle down and goes to him as he sways*) What are you doing here? Here, hold me. William! What are you trying to do? Do you want something? You only had to call me . . .

He collapses into a chair, sweating with pain, moaning, head turned from her

William. Don't. Don't. Just a moment. I know where there's some brandy . . .

She hurries off. There is a pause and then she returns

Here, drink this.

He tries to resist

Here you idiot. Or shall I fetch Mary?

He drinks. Christina fetches a rug from his bed and wraps him in it, then sees to the fire. He sits, huddled, staring, still agonized

Are you all right?

William (*whispering, angrily*) Oh, stop fussing. You didn't have to interfere did you?

Christina But what were you doing?

William You could see couldn't you? Just walking about.

Christina But WHY? However will your leg mend if you walk on it? You know what Dr. Porter said. What were you trying to do? (*And as she asks she sees in his face the answer*) You—you mean, that—that's what you want! (*Appalled*) Is—is—that why you—you! . . . William, is it true?

William I want it to set stiff, with the joint locked. Dr Porter said that is what would happen if I walked on it before it was ready

Christina You are wicked! You are mad! Have you REALLY thought what it will mean? All your life?

William Yes, of course I've thought. I've had plenty of time to think, haven't I? And I think it's worth it, and you won't make me change my mind.

Christina Just so that you don't have to ride? Is it really as bad as that?

William Hunting is, yes.

Christina I don't believe it. Not to have a stiff leg all your life. You'll be a cripple.

William It will be all right for you. You're a girl. You'll be given Sweet-briar, and you can go through the gates and Dick will look after you, like he did this afternoon. But Father is such a maniac—I cannot stand facing him night after night with all that claptrap, and his knowing I am afraid. He has never been afraid in his life, he does not know how it feels. And if I cannot ride he will wash his hands of me. I shall be left in peace. He will hate me but that will make no difference.

Christina But it's only for a few years, till you're old enough to do as you please. And your leg will be for ever.

William I know. But I've made up my mind. In any case, Dr Porter said he thought it was going to mend stiff. That's what he's been shaking his head about. He told me on no account to put it out of bed, to give it the best chance, and that's what gave me the idea. I'm only helping on a bit what's already happening.

Christina It is wicked, what you are doing.

William It's my life. And you can't guess what I feel about hunting. I am a coward. I am terrified. And why should I be reminded what a coward I am four days a week for the next seven years? You just think about it —you don't know how-I feel. . . . (*His voice chokes to a stop. Christina stares hard at him, shocked*) . . . You see, I shall be able to fly with a stiff leg. It will just mean adjusting the rudder bar a bit . . . It will make no difference to what I really want to do.

Christina You are mad.

William You're not going to tell anyone about this? (*A pause*) Are you?

Christina I—I don't know.

William If you tell anyone, if you INTERFERE . . .

Christina (*nervously*) What? It's not to be unkind, William, don't you see? But what you're doing . . .

William I have thought about it. I know what I'm doing. I promise you, if you interfere, I—oh, I know! I know what I shall do. If you tell Mary, or Mark, or Father, I shall tell Father that Dick poaches in our covert. It is true, I have seen him, and Dick knows that I know. And if you tell anybody about me, I shall tell Father, and Dick will get a flogging and be dismissed. Mark used the same threat over you, not to tell about Treasure. Now it's my turn.

Christina You wouldn't!

William I promise you I would. This means far more to me than Dick's welfare.

Christina Oh, William, you are raving. Get back to bed. I will help you. We'll talk about it in the morning.

William In the morning, it will be the same.

Christina Oh, you stubborn beast! Come on, get up, while you still can. If you faint here I shall HAVE to call Mary. . . . Come on, we can't talk all night. Get up, if you're so determined to walk. I can't carry you . . . (*She tries to help him up. In intense pain, he sinks on to the chair again*) See what you're doing to yourself! It would serve you right if you never walk again, like your father!

K. M. PEYTON

FLIBBERTY AND THE PENGUIN

MR SILLY CUCKOO / MRS SILLY CUCKOO

Young Penguin and Flibberty, a genial goblin, are searching for Young Penguin's parents. On their travels they meet, among other characters, two Silly Cuckoos busy practising their Spring song

Part of the forest

Mrs Silly Cuckoo, bossy and irritable, enters calling

Mrs Silly Cuckoo Mr Silly Cuckoo! Mr Silly Cuckoo!! "Urry 'urry up!".

Mr Silly Cuckoo enters breathlessly, with a shopping bag

Mr Silly Cuckoo Mrs Silly Cuckoo, I'm 'urry 'urriying as fast as my leggy pegs will go.

Mrs Silly Cuckoo At lasty-wasty! Where on earthy-wearthy have you beeny-weeny?

Mr Silly Cuckoo I'm sorry, Mrs Silly Cuckoo. But I've got all your shoppy-wopping to carry-warry.

Mrs Silly Cuckoo Then put it downy-wowny for a seccy-weccy, Mr Silly Cuckoo. Oh, you're such a silly-willy-billy. Wool! (*She hands him a ball of wool and starts knitting*)

Mr Silly Cuckoo I'm sorry-worry, Mrs Silly Cuckoo. (*He puts down the shopping*) I'm a teeny weeny bit hot and bother-wothered today.

Mrs Silly Cuckoo Ah! That's because it will soon be the first day of springy-wingy.

Mr Silly Cuckoo Of course. How luviwuviduvly! The first day of springy-wingy.

They giggle

Mrs Silly Cuckoo Warmer weather round the corner-worner.

Mr Silly Cuckoo How excitiwiting. Soon I'll be the first cuckoo of springy-wingy. Everyone will hear me singalinging my song and know that springywingy's here. Ah!

Mrs Silly Cuckoo (*after a stunned pause*) I beg your pardon?

Mr Silly Cuckoo (*delighted*) I shall be the first cuckoo of springywingy.

Mrs Silly Cuckoo (*furiously*) Oh no you willy notwot.

Mr Silly Cuckoo But, Mrs Silly Cuckoo ...

Mrs Silly Cuckoo *I* shallywall.

Mr Silly Cuckoo But you were firstywirsty *last* year!

Mrs Silly Cuckoo Exactlywactly. I was *so* goodygood last year that I shall be firstywirsty again *this* year.

Mr Silly Cuckoo But that's not fair. It's my turnywurn. Any anyway, last year you sang your cuckoos so badly that no-one heard them till the *fourth* day of springywingy.

Mrs Silly Cuckoo You cheeky-beaky bird! I'd like to hear you do better-wetter.

Mr Silly Cuckoo Very well—listen. (*He clears his throat and then, in a rather cracked voice, sings "Cuckoo, cuckoo, cuckoo", but reverses the musical notes*) How's thatywat?

Mrs Silly Cuckoo Terriwerrible! You go up instead of down an down instead of up. It's "la la", not "la la". (*She "La's" the correct cuckoo notes*)

Mr Silly Cuckoo Well, you show me then, if you're so cleverdever.

Mrs Silly Cuckoo Very Well. (*She clears her throat and then, getting the notes right, reverses the word*) Oo-cuck, Oo-cuck, Oo-cuck. How's thatywat?

Mr Silly Cuckoo (*speaking*) Oo-cuck, oo-cuck? Oh, Mrs Silly Cuckoo, that's terriwerrible! It's *cuck-oo*, not oo-cuck.

Mrs Silly Cuckoo Well, it's better than yours, anyway. Let's try againywen, till we get it right.

SONG: OO-CUCK!

Both (*singing together*)

> We're two silly-billy cuckoos
> We don't know our cucks from our oos
> If we can't sing properwoperly
> When winter turns to spring
> How will you hear the luviduvly news?

Mrs Silly Cuckoo	Oo cuck
Mr Silly Cuckoo	Cuckoo
Both	Will we never get it rightywight?
Mrs Silly Cuckoo	Oo cuck
Mr Silly Cuckoo	Cuckoo
Both	Pracywactising all nightywight
Mrs Silly Cuckoo	Oo cuck
Mr Silly Cuckoo	Cuckoo
Both	It's wrong againywen I fear
	And the first day of springywing
	Will soon be here
	We're two sillybilly cuckoos
	We can't sing our cuckoo song
Mr Silly Cuckoo	I go up instead of downywown
Mrs Silly Cuckoo	I oo when I should cuck
Both	And we've not gotiwoty very long.
Mrs Silly Cuckoo	Oo cuck
Mr Silly Cuckoo	Cuckoo
Both	Will we never get it rightywight?
Mrs Silly Cuckoo	Oo cuck
Mr Silly Cuckoo	Cuckoo
Both	Pracywactising all nightywight
Mrs Silly Cuckoo	Oo cuck
Mr Silly Cuckoo	Cuckoo

Both   It's wrong againywen I fear
                         And the first day of springywing
                         Will soon be here
Mrs Silly Cuckoo Oo cuck
Mr Silly Cuckoo Cuckoo!

DAVID WOOD

THE FLIPPERTY-FLY-BY-NIGHT

MISTRESS GUBBINS / TWINKLE

Mistress Gubbins rather takes to Twinkle, the flipperty-fly-by-night, but knows she must hide him from her grumpy husband. The scene is a cosy cottage kitchen, during the time of fairy-tales

Mistress Gubbins takes ingredients from the cupboard and begins preparing the hot drink

A faint, tapping sound is heard

Mistress Gubbins What's that? (*Tapping continues*) Is that you, Gregory? (*More tapping*) It's outside. Oh dear me, not another caller. It's someone tapping on the window! (*Going to the window she opens it a little*) Is anyone there?

Twinkle (*outside*) Yes, me.

Mistress Gubbins Who's "me"?

Twinkle (*appearing at the window*) Me. I fell. I fell miles. And I've bumped my knee.

Mistress Gubbins Poor lamb! Is it bad?

Twinkle Yes, it is. I'd better come in, hadn't I—and show you?

He climbs in at the window. He is a quaint, elf-like little creature, wearing a tight-fitting suit of silver-grey

Mistress Gubbins (*looking at it*) My! There's a nasty place. I'll put some ointment on it. (*She gets ointment from cupboard and puts some on Twinkle's knee*)

Twinkle (*interested*) Shall I have a bandage?

Mistress Gubbins I'll just put on a piece of plaster. (*Does so*) There! That will soon be well.

Twinkle You're a nice person. What's your name?

Mistress Gubbins Gubbins. Mistress Gubbins, they call me. And what's your name?

Twinkle Twinkle.

Mistress Gubbins That's a pretty name. And what were you doing, Twinkle, to get a nasty knee like that?

Twinkle I fell off the star.

Mistress Gubbins Fell off the—You're never a—a—? now what did Gregory call them—a Flipperty-Fly-By-Night?

Twinkle Of course. It's fun riding the shooting stars, but you fall off sometimes. I've never fallen off before. What's the matter? Why are you looking at me like that?

Mistress Gubbins It's nothing, love. Now I think you'd better run along home.

118

Twinkle You can't "run along" with a hurt knee. Besides, it's too far and I don't know the way. This is a nice place. Can't I stay here?

Mistress Gubbins I'm afraid not, dearie.

Twinkle Why not?

Mistress Gubbins You see, dearie, it's my Gregory—

Twinkle Who's he? Your little boy?

Mistress Gubbins I haven't any little boys. Nor girls either. Never had—more's the pity. Gregory is my husband. And he doesn't hold with Flipperty-fly-by-Nights.

Twinkle Why not?

Mistress Gubbins Well—he just doesn't.

Twinkle When you're cold and hungry and your knee hurts and you don't know the way home—it isn't much use just not holding with anyone.

Mistress Gubbins I know, love. If it were for me to say you should stay, and welcome. But Gregory—well there—that's how it is. Don't cry, love. Don't now.

Twinkle I'm not crying. I simply m-mentioned it was n-not m-much use not h-holding with people.

Mistress Gubbins All right, dearie. You shall stay just for tonight. (*Opening linen cupboard door*) You can sleep in here. Only for tonight, mind.

Twinkle It looks cosy.

Mistress Gubbins You'll be as snug as a bird in its nest. But you must stay quiet. As quiet as quiet can be till morning. Then, when Gregory has gone off to work, I'll let you out and you can be off before he comes home again.

Twinkle *After* breakfast?

Mistress Gubbins If you're good you shall have breakfast with me before you go. Hark! That's my Gregory calling. Into the cupboard, quick. In a moment, Gregory.

Twinkle (*at cupboard door*) I usually have supper as well as breakfast.

Mistress Gubbins Didn't you have supper before you went riding on the star?

Twinkle Well—yes. But it was a long time ago.

Mistress Gubbins Ah well! So it would be. (*She takes a bun from the cupboard and gives it him*) Eat it slowly and don't make crumbs. (*She shepherds him into the linen-cupboard and tucks him up*) There! Night-night, love. Sleep tight.

Twinkle Night-night. You hold with Flipperty-fly-by-Nights, don't you?

Mistress Gubbins Bless your heart, of course I do. Coming Gregory.

Mistress Gubbins closes the linen-cupboard and hurries off taking the hot drink with her

MARGARET GIBBS

GONE AWAY TO WORK

MARY / KEVIN

An unpublished play about a problem family, where the father is in prison. Mary, the oldest child, fears that her brother is getting into trouble. With her mother so tired, overworked and anxious about money, Mary takes on many responsibilities. Mary is about 15, Kevin, 13. The scene takes place in the kitchen which has a mean and depressed atmosphere, reflecting poverty but nevertheless is clean and homely

Kevin has given his mother some money because he knows how hard up she is. She has returned it, and gone into the kitchen, leaving Kevin and Mary in the living room. Kevin looks at the money in his hand, crushes it into his clenched fist and throws it down. Mary looks at Kevin and picks up the notes

Mary There's little enough of it about.

Kevin I don't want it.

Mary I'll have it then.

Kevin No, you won't. It's for Mum.

Mary You shouldn't have done it the way you did.

Kevin What do you mean?

Mary Oh, I know about it. I was in here when Mum found it in her bag.

Kevin I wanted it to be a surprise.

Mary It was a surprise all right. Where did you get it?

Kevin Mind your own business.

Mary You nicked it, didn't you?

Kevin I saved it.

Mary Like hell you did.

Kevin I bloody saved it I tell you.

Mary She thinks you nicked it and so do I.

Kevin Well, you're wrong, Clever Dick. I saved it out of my paper round, see.

Mary What, with your fags and your football?

Kevin Why don't you keep your great big ugly nose out of it?

Mary Because our mum's got enough on her plate without you making it worse.

Kevin How am I making it worse by giving her money when she needs it?

Mary It isn't the money.

Kevin What is it then?

Mary You should treat her kind. And do what she says.

Kevin Like what?

Mary Like taking that money back to wherever you nicked it from.

Kevin I never nicked it. And if I did why should I do what she wants after the way she's treated me?

Mary How has she treated you? What have you got against her?

Kevin Treating me like a baby. Pretending. Why doesn't she tell me the truth?

Mary About what?

Kevin About dad, that's what. Mary, you know about it, don't you?

Mary Yes . . . How did you know?

Kevin I thought it was funny him going off like that without saying anything about it beforehand. I never really believed that story about going away to work. I always knew there was something fishy. Then Ted Hunter said that his mum wouldn't let me go round his house any more and when I asked why, he showed me the thing in the newspaper. (*He pulls a crumpled paper cutting from his pocket*)

Mary Throw that thing away, Kevin, you don't want to keep it.

Kevin (*screwing up the paper*) Why didn't she tell me?

Mary Can't you understand, Kevin? He asked her not to tell us. I expect he feels ashamed. Wouldn't you be?

Kevin I suppose so.

Mary So you see how difficult it was for Mum. We've got to help her all we can. Can't you see how awful it would be for her if you got into trouble as well.

Kevin I'm not in any trouble, I tell you.

Mary Was that really your own money, Kevin? Kevin, you've got to tell me the truth even if you don't tell Mum.

Kevin Of course it was. Well, most of it.

Mary How much of it?

Kevin Five pounds. I borrowed the rest.

Mary Borrowed? Who from?

Kevin I'm going to pay it back out of my paper round.

Mary Did Mr Evans lend it to you then?

Kevin Well, not exactly. It's just that some of the customers pay me when I deliver. I'll pay it over the next five weeks. Nobody will ever know.

Mary If that is the truth, and you want to help mum, you know what to do. Lend her the five that's yours. Just lend it to her, not give it. She'll find it easier to accept that way, even if she can't pay it back. Take the money, and give it in to Mr Evans first thing tomorrow morning. Say you collected it yesterday morning and forgot it was in your pocket.

Kevin She needs the money more than Mr Evans.

Mary I know she needs the money, but she needs something else much more. She needs not to have any more trouble, like you being taken to Court for stealing. Can't you see that, Kevin?

Kevin I shan't get caught.

Mary That's what Dad thought. Please, Kevin.

Kevin I never did it for myself, did I?

Mary That doesn't make it right, Kevin. I'll never ask you another thing if you'll do this for me. Not for me, for Mum. Please, Kevin.

Mother, offstage, calls "Tea"

Coming. Kevin. . .

Kevin O.K. I suppose you're right. I'll do it . . .

Mary Thanks.   DAVID ROWLEY

THE GRANDMOTHER STONE

PHILIP / MARIE

The paperback title of this is "The Stone of Terror". It is set in the Channel Islands in the 17th century, a time when there was much witch-hunting. Philip Hoskyn is drawn toward the fiery, gypsy-like Marie Perchon, the girl they all torment and call "Witch-brat". It is an exciting story of love, witchcraft and adventure

Marie is walking behind Philip. He stops. She pauses a moment, then seems about to speak, but instead drops him a half-mocking curtsy, and walks on without a word

Philip Marie . . .

She turns, but obviously wants to go

Marie why are you always running away?

Marie Why should I not? There is no-one wishes my company?

Philip Foolishness! I want to talk with you. (*Pulling her wrist, he makes her sit by the roadside with him*) What a strange girl you are. I would wish to be friends.

Marie (*sullenly*) I have no friends. I hate people and they hate me.

Philip But why, Marie? They can't all be like Tom Carre.

Marie (*spitting*) He is a brute beast—a roistering filthy bully. But they all hate me too. You are a stranger and do not know. You will soon be like them. I am Annette Perchon's niece.

Philip Whatever your aunt is, why should I not like YOU?

Marie You know what she is.

Philip (*boldly*) I know what people say. But why should I believe them?

Marie Because it is true. My Aunt Perchon is a witch. They are all afraid of her because she has the power. She can curse and make it come true.

Philip How can you know?

Marie There is a man on Brecqhou.

Philip The coney island?

Marie (*nodding*) He lived on Serq once, and he had a wife. The woman made my aunt angry. I do not know how. It was before I was born. But my Aunt Perchon cursed her and she died. She has often told me. (*With pride and some fear in her voice*) I think—I think this was when she first knew she was a witch.

Philip Maybe the women would have died even if your aunt had not cursed her.

Marie You! You try to talk like your grandfather. The Church knows that there are witches, but he will not have it so. Once I heard the minister himself tell him that he is little better than an infidel.

Philip (*indignantly*) He is not. My grandfather is a good man. But he will not believe evil without cause. He says your aunt is miserable.

Marie (*savagely*) She ought to be miserable. She makes me wretched too.

Philip Is she unkind to you then?

Marie She beats me for every fault. Or for no fault at all when she is angry. I am a burden to her. She says so. And she makes me do things.

Philip (*noticing her sly, sideways glance*) What kind of things?

Marie Never you meddle with them. But—(*Whispering*) she says I must do them or the Stone will be angry.

Philip stares at her, horrified—then realizes she is more to be pitied than feared

Philip Listen, Marie. You must not do these things, whatever they are. Pretend to do them if you must, but don't let her turn your heart to them. I will be your friend and help you if you will let me.

Marie (*flushing*) No one has ever spoken to me kindly as you do. . . . You will grow like the others. But I think—I think I shall remember. (*She shakes herself as if coming out of a dream*) Why have you come here?

Philip My mother sent me.

Marie Does she not want you, then?

Philip She loves me. But my grandfather wished me to come.

Marie Why did she not come too?

Philip She is not strong. She could not have made such a journey.

Marie Then why did you leave her? (*She is purposely provoking him*)

Philip Would you have me disobey my mother? She has Abby, my cousin, who lives with her.

Marie This Abby—how old is she?

Philip Only a little older than I.

Marie Is she pretty?

Philip (*laughing*) I don't know. I have never thought of it.

Marie (*springing up, jealous, teasing*) Perhaps she loves you too. She loves you and you left her. You love your mother and you left her. Love is stupid. Stupid philip!

Philip (*jumping up, catching her and shaking her, as she twists and scratches*) Stop Marie. You are a foolish girl, a savage. It is nearly time I went home. I will go back with you first.

Marie (*sharply*) No. . . . Yes. Come and see where I live, Philip Hoskyn. . . . (*They start to move, she dragging him, then stopping suddenly*) Then you will soon see why they told you to have naught to do with me.

MARGARET GREAVES

HOW JAN KLAASSEN CURED THE KING

KATRYN / LANDLORD

This was originally a puppet play but acts perfectly well by humans. Jan and Katryn, a lively young married couple with a new baby are continually in debt to their Landlord

It has a traditional Dutch folk tale flavour to it, and needs clear, bold playing

Katryn (*very agitated*) Tell me, has anyone here seen my dear husband, Jan Klaassen? You haven't seen him? No? Oh dear, oh dear, where can he be? He went off early this morning with a sack of potatoes on his back. To sell in the town, you understand. A lovely sack of potatoes. And "Katryn", he says, that's my name, Katryn . . . "Katryn," he says, "I'll be back for supper. Oh yes, my love," says he, "I'll be back for supper, with my purse full of money for I'll sell these fine potatoes for a tidy penny or my name's not Jan Klaassen." Yes, that's what he said. And here it is, long gone supper-time, and no sign of him. . . .

Katryn shades her eyes with left hand, and looks left, then shades her eyes with right hand, and looks right

(*Mopping her tears now with her gay little apron*) Oh dear, where can he be? I *am* so worried. You see, we have no money left, no money at all. And our shoes need mending, and my bucket has a hole in it. And the baby wants a new coat, and oh, I would so like a new hat. (*She mops away more tears*) But worst, worst of all, we have no money to pay the rent of our little house. And between you and me, our Landlord has a heart of stone . . .

Oh dear, Katryn doesn't see what we see—the Landlord himself has stalked in, and there he stands now, glowering at Katryn

(*Going straight on, quite unaware of scowling Landlord*) Oh yes, our Landlord has a heart of stone . . . of cold, cold stone . . .

Landlord savagely blows his nose. Katryn jumps

(*Startled*) Oh . . .! Why, it's you, Mr Landlord.
Landlord (*grim*) Yes, it's me. Rent, please! (*He holds out his hand*)
Katryn (*warmly shaking hands*) How are you, Mr Landlord? And how is your dear wife? Well, I hope? And all your dear clever children? How are they?
Landlord (*grim as ever*) My dear wife's well. So are my dear children. And I'll feel well, too, when you pay me the rent you owe me. (*He pulls out a large account book, opens it, and studies it. Consulting his book*) You now owe me: one, two, three, four, five, six, SEVEN weeks' rent . . .

124

Katryn (*dismayed*) Seven?

Landlord (*thumping book*) Seven! Seven weeks' rent. And seven threes are
. . . um . . . seven threes are . . . twenty-one!

Katryn (*even more dismayed*) Oh, dear, are they? Are you *sure*?

Landlord Seven threes ARE twenty-one. They always have been. And
that's what you owe me, seven times three guilders. Twenty-one guilders.

Katryn (*thinking hard*) Twenty-one guilders. Ah yes, of course. For the
rent. For the rent, of course.

Landlord Yes, Mistress Katryn. The RENT!

Katryn (*earnestly*) Then of course, we must pay you. We certainly must
pay you. Of course, we must.

Landlord Good. (*He closes book and holds out his hand*)

Katryn (*not even noticing it*) In fact, I was just telling these dear people here
that I'm expecting Jan back any minute now, wasn't I, my dears? Yes,
any minute now, and my dear husband will be back with a big purse
full of money. He's gone to town to sell a sack of potatoes, lovely new
potatoes. So you come back to-morrow, Mr Landlord, and we'll pay
the rent. Every cent of it.

Landlord (*sour*) That's what you said last week, Mistress Katryn.

Katryn (*surprised*) Did I?

Landlord And the week before . . .

Katryn (*very surprised*) Did I?

Landlord And the week before that again.

Katryn (*full of admiration*) Och! What a marvellous memory you have,
Mr Landlord!

Landlord Yes, and I remember best of all that you now owe me seven
weeks' rent. So I'll be obliged, Mistress Katryn, if you will kindly . . .

Katryn Sh-sh-sh!

*She holds up one finger, and listens. Landlord listens too. From the house
comes a distant wail: "Ma-ma! Ma-ma!"*

(*Delighted*) Oh dear, that's the baby! I really must run in and see to him.
I know you'll forgive me if I fly now. So nice to see you again! Good-bye,
Mr Landlord, good-bye!

*She flies in, door closes behind her. Landlord glowers at house, and then
turns to audience, and glowers even more savagely*

Landlord Cross, am I? In a temper, am !? Of course I'm cross! Of course
I'm in a temper! Here I am, the respectable Landlord of this desirable
residence, two rooms up, two rooms down, best wooden shutters, nice
tidy garden. So you'd think I'd get a nice, tidy rent, wouldn't you?
And do I? No, I do not. That good-for-nothing Jan Klaassen owes me
seven weeks' rent, twenty-one guilders. TWENTY-ONE guilders.
(*Savagely*) And I'll get it, yes, I'll get it, or I'll turn him out. Yes, out
he'll go, *and* that chatty wife of his, *and* his howling baby! Out they'll
all go, all three of them.

ANTONIA RIDGE

THE INSECT PLAY

MR CRICKET / MRS CRICKET

Written in 1923 by two Czechoslovakian brothers this play has this rhyme printed at the beginning:

> *So, naturalists observe, a flea*
> *Has smaller fleas that on him prey;*
> *And these have smaller still to bite 'em,*
> *And so proceed AD INFINITUM*

You can look at the play in different ways and the political feeling need not concern you. The characters may be played fairly human with insect traits or can be quite fantasised as suits you best. The crickets are an adoring young couple, newly wed and expecting their first cricket

Mr Cricket (*off stage*) Look out, darling—take care you don't stumble. Here we are—here we are. Oopsidaisy! This is where we live—this is our new little home. Careful—You haven't hurt yourself, have you?

Mr and Mrs Cricket enter

Mrs Cricket No, Cricket, don't be absurd.

Mr Cricket But darling, you must be careful—When you're expecting—and now open the peephole—look—How do you like it?

Mrs Cricket Oh, darling, how tied I am!

Mr Cricket Sit down, darling, sit down. My popsy must take great care of herself.

Mrs Cricket What a long way—And all the move! Oh, men never know half the trouble moving is.

Mr Cricket Oh darling, come, come—Look, darling, look.

Mrs Cricket Now don't get cross, you horrid man.

Mr Cricket I won't say another word, really I won't. Fancy, Mrs Cricket won't take care of herself, and in her state too—What do you think of her?

Mrs Cricket You naughty man—how can you joke about it?

Mr Cricket But darling, I'm so happy. Just fancy, all the little crickets, the noise, the chirping—(*He imitates the noise and laughs*)

Mrs Cricket You—you silly boy—wants to be a great big Daddy, eh?

Mr Cricket And don't you want to be a Mummy too?—my Popsy?

Mrs Cricket Yes'm does! Is this our new home?

Mr Cricket Our little nest. Commodious little villa residence.

Mrs Cricket Will it be dry? Who built it?

Mr Cricket Why, goodness me, another Cricket lived here years ago.

Mrs Cricket Fancy, and has he moved?

Mr Cricket Ha, ha—Yes, he's moved. Don't you know where to? Guess.

126

Mrs Cricket I don't know—What a long time you take saying anything— Do tell me, Cricket, quickly.

Mr Cricket Well, yesterday a bird got him—Snap, snip, snap. So we're moving into his house. By Jove, what a slice of luck!

Mrs Cricket Gobbled him up alive? How horrible!

Mr Cricket Eh? A godsend for us. I did laugh. Tralala, etc. We'll put up a plate. (*He puts up a plate with "Mr. Cricket, musician"*) Where shall we put it? More to the right? Higher?

Mrs Cricket And you saw him eaten?

Mr. Cricket I'm telling you—like that—snap snip!

Mrs Cricket Horrible! Cricket, I have such a queer feeling.

Mr Cricket Good heavens—Perhaps it's—no, it couldn't be, not yet!

Mrs Cricket Oh dear, I'm so frightened.

Mr Cricket Nothing to be frightened of, dear—Every lady——

Mrs Cricket It's all very well for you to talk—Cricket, will you always love me?

Mr Cricket Of course, darling—Dear me, don't cry—come, love.

Mrs Cricket Show me how he swallowed him—Snip, snap.

Mr Cricket Snip, snap,

Mrs Cricket Oh, how funny! (*She has hysterics*)

Mr Cricket Well, well. There's nothing to cry about. (*Sits beside her*) We'll furnish this place beautifully. And as soon as we can run to it, we'll put up some——

Mrs Cricket Curtains?

Mr Cricket Curtains, of course! How clever of you to think of it. Give me a kiss.

Mrs Cricket Never mind that now—Don't be silly.

Mr Cricket Of course I'm silly. Guess what I've brought?

Mrs Cricket Curtains!

Mr. Cricket No, something smaller—Where did I——?

Mrs Cricket Quick, quick, let me see.

Mr Cricket takes out a rattle

Oh, how sweet, Cricket! Give it to me.

Mr Cricket (*singing*)
　　　　When Dr Stork had brought their child,
　　　　　　Their teeny-weeny laddy,
　　　　All day about the cradle smiled
　　　　　　His mumsy and his daddy:
　　　　And "Cricket, cricket, cricket,
　　　　　　You pretty little thing"—
　　　　Is now the song that all day long
　　　　　　They sing, sing, sing.

Mrs Cricket Lend it me, darling—Oh, daddy—I'm so pleased. Rattle it.

Mr Cricket Darling.

Mrs Cricket (*singing*) Cricket, cricket, cricket!

Mr Cricket Now I must run round a little—let people know I am here.

Mrs Cricket (*singing*)
　　　　And "Cricket, cricket, cricket,
　　　　　　You pretty little thing . . ."

Mr Cricket I must get some introductions, fix up orders, have a look round. Give me the rattle, I'll use it on my way.

Mrs Cricket And what about me? I want it.

Mr Cricket Very well, darling.

Mrs Cricket You won't leave me long——

Mr Cricket Rattle for me if you want me. And I expect a neighbour will be coming along. Have a chat with him, about the children, and all that, you know.

Mrs Cricket You bad boy.

Mr Cricket Now, darling, be careful. Won't be long, my pet.

K. AND C. CAPEK

THE LEGEND OF CARCASSONE

LOUAN / JEHAN

The City of Carcassone has been under seige for 5 years and the people are shabby and starving. Louan's mother conceives an ingenious, bold plan to outwit the soldiers of Charlemagne. It involves the fattening of a pig. Unfortunately Louan's friend, the girl Jehan, lets this secret out and then, frightened, runs away to the woods. Louan goes in search of her.

Time: 771–814 AD

A figure appears. It is Louan. Keeping cautiously to the side, he calls softly

Louan Jehan!

Jehan gasps with fright. He calls again

Jehan!
Jehan Louan! Oh, Louan, here I am, over here!

Louan darts over to her

Louan Thank goodness! I thought I'd never find you.
Jehan I got lost—and the woods are alive with soldiers. Louan, I'm terrified!
Louan So am I! But at least I know the way. Come on!
Jehan But they'll see us!
Louan (*pointing* L) We have to make for that clump of trees. Keep close to the ground!
Jehan I will!
Louan (*he takes a look round*) Now!
Jehan Oh dear!
Louan Follow me! (*They start* L, *then Louan stops suddenly looking back* Back quickly! They're coming!
Jehan Oh!

They dash back to the log and crouch down in front of it

Several soldiers run on upstage R *not seeing them*

Jehan Louan, what can be happening?
Louan (*hurrying up and looking off* L) It's the plan! And we won't be back in time.
Jehan (*joining him*) What do you mean? Look! It's your mother! Oh I hope she catches the pig!
Louan She does not wish to catch it.
Jehan What? But she must. If it falls over the edge it will be lost! That enormous pig!

129

Louan Ah, there goes Mother! And look, the soldiers by the moat are watching!

Jehan Louan! They will shoot at her.

Louan No, they are too interested in what is happening. There! The pig is running nearer and nearer the edge!

Jehan Oh your poor mother—how she is wailing.

Louan Yes, she is acting her part well.

Jehan Acting!

The shouting in the distance gets louder

Louan Yes. It is all part of the plan you see—ah!—the pig has fallen off the wall.

A splash is heard in the distance

Jehan It's swimming! It will get to the bank, Louan, and we shall have lost it. Is your mother mad?

Louan See, now she is leaning over the wall.

Jehan But, Louan, she doesn't seem to realize what a loss it is. Look, she shrugged and turned away—as if she had a dozen like it.

Louan Don't you see, Jehan. That's the idea. The soldiers have seen the whole thing—so what will they think?

Jehan Well, if they find such a fat pig——

Louan They'll say, "Here we've been trying to starve this city into surrender for five years and they can still feed their pigs like *this*. We might as well go home".

Jehan (*delightedly*) Of course, Louan. They will think we have secret supplies of food. What a wonderful idea!

Louan See, the soldiers have dragged the pig from the water—they will take it to Charlemagne, that's sure! (*Jehan moves downstage in sudden consternation*) How's that for a trick, Jehan? (*Turning, to find she has moved away*) Why, what's the matter?

Jehan Oh! Oh, Louan! It can't work!

Louan Of course it can! They will be fooled into thinking we can hold out indefinitely.

Jehan No, Louan! Your mother's plan can never work!

Louan (*incredulously*) What?

Jehan It will be all my fault! Oh Louan! (*She weeps*)

Louan How could it possibly be?

Jehan It just won't work—I know!

Louan (*shrewdly*) I believe—you met someone in the woods, didn't you?

Jehan (*wailing*) Oh!

Louan (*gripping her wrist*) Didn't you?

Jehan Yes!

Louan (*appalled*) And you told them the city was destitute!

Jehan Yes.

Louan Who was it? (*Jehan shakes her head, Louan grips her shoulders*) Did they tell *you* anything?

Jehan Yes, but I promised to say nothing! So did he!

Louan But you must!

Jehan I'll say nothing!

Louan But you believe he'll break *his* word?

Jehan He may not mean to—but when he sees the pig—he'll know it's a trick.

Louan And my mother risked her life!

Jehan How was I to know?

Louan There is only one way to make up—you must tell everything you know to the Sheriff.

Jehan I will not break my word—not this time!

Louan But if *he* does?

Jehan Even if he *does*, I'll keep *my* word.

Louan But Jehan——

Jehan (*running off* DL) It was you who taught me so!

ERIC NEWTON and JEAN MCDONNELL

THE LEGEND OF SCARFACE AND BLUE WATER

SCARFACE / BLUE WATER

This play developed from project work on the theme of the American Indian and all the ideas are based on truth. Blue Water is the beautiful young daughter of Chief Red Cloud. She is serene, obedient, dignified. Scarface is a young farmer of the Kiowa tribe, who has lived alone since childhood. He is proud, in spite of his poverty and his scarred cheek

Scarface (*shouting*) I am Scarface from the Sand Hills and I come to speak with the Chief's daughter, Blue Water. I ask that we may talk face to face.

Blue Water (*from the tent*) I am Blue Water, daughter of Chief Red Cloud and will speak with Scarface of the Sand Hills. What is your message?

Scarface I am not like the young hunters of your village, but I am brave. I . . . I . . .

He cannot speak any more for Blue Water comes out of the tent and he sees her for the first time and is overwhelmed with her beauty

Blue Water Your words were as quick as lightning before and now your tongue is as still as the windless summer. Speak again young Brave. I *will* listen. I hear even the silence.

Scarface I am a poor planter who must plough his corn into barren soil. My people are no more. I came to ask Blue Water's hand because I was challenged. *Now* I ask the hand of Blue Water, who stands as alone as I, in this land of plenty, *because* I loved her.

Blue Water Your words run as deep as the river. You see the shadows in my heart. (*She looks at the scar on his check and touches it*) I feel what you are feeling, and see the shadow on your check. Yes. (*Pause*) I would marry you, Scarface. The Braves of my village are forbidden to me. No other could I choose, but only a stranger such as you. Now we must wait for a sign from the Sun God since I cannot wed anyone without his consent.

Scarface (*with strength*) I will not wait for this sign, but I will go to the Sun God and seek his consent. To find an answer for you without question, I would journey farther than the sky.

Blue Water We must set a sign. If the Sun God consents, he will heal the scar on your cheek.

Scarface Where will I find him, Blue Water? Which is the way to go?

Blue Water You must go to the West where his bed lies. Far over the hills to the edge of the sky.

Scarface Then I will find the home of the Sun God and we will wed in His Dawn.

Scarface slowly exits to stage R as Blue Water bids farewell

NIKKI MARVIN

THE OWL AND THE PUSSYCAT WENT TO SEE . . .

PUSSYCAT/OWL

The opening scene of a very funny play based loosely on Edward Lear's famous poem. The Owl is lovable, warm and gentle, but not over-bright. The Pussycat is quick-witted, lively, very nimble and practical. They are in a boat and have with them a huge £5 note, a large jar of honey and Owl's guitar

Owl O lovely Pussy,
     O Pussy my love,
     What a beautiful
     Pussy you are, you are, you are,
     What a beautiful pussy you are.
Pussycat (*speaks*) And you're so very elegant.
Owl (*speaks*) Am I really?
Pussycat Yes.

Owl and Pussycat laugh

Owl (*after a pause*) Why don't we get married?
Pussycat What?
Owl I love you so much—let's get married—now.
Pussycat Eh?
Owl This very minute.
Pussycat But how can we?
Owl It's quite simple really. We ask a friendly vicar to . . .
Pussycat In the middle of the sea?
Owl Oh. Good point. No friendly vicars out here—only fish.
Pussycat Exactly. (*After a thinking pause*) Let's look for one!
Owl What, a fish?
Pussycat No, silly, a vicar.
Owl Yes! (*Doubtful*) Where?
Pussycat Anywhere.
Owl Then we'll keep going till we find somewhere.
Pussycat (*remembering*) And a ring—you have to give me a ring.
Owl But you're not on the telephone.
Pussycat A *wedding* ring.
Owl Yes, of course. A ring and someone to marry us. That's all we want.
Pussycat Let's hope we find them soon.
Owl Then you *will* marry me?
Pussycat Of course . . .

Owl and Pussycat wave and the boat sails on for a year and a day

Owl Well, we've arrived—somewhere.
Pussycat Looks like an island.

133

Owl Funny trees. Bet there are ghosts and beasties and things hiding them . . .

Pussycat Stop it.

Owl Just waiting to—pounce. (*He pounces on Pussycat*)

Pussycat (*taken by surprise*) Ah! Don't be silly. Let's go on land. We can try to find a vicar there.

Owl It's a bit dark to start vicar-hunting.

Pussycat I know, silly. We'll rest under the trees and start looking in the morning . . . (*Whispering*) Come on.

Pussycat climbs over, helped by Owl, and tiptoes through the "water" to the "dry" land

Ooh, it's cold; mind your tail feathers.

Owl climbs over and gets his feet wet

Owl Ooooh! (*He joins Pussycat*)

Pussycat (*whispering*) Shhh. Pass me the luggage.

Owl (*whispering*) Right.

Owl goes back to the boat, getting his feet wet again

Pussycat It's ever so dark.

Owl (*struggling back with the honey*) I don't know why we had to bring this with us—it's so heavy.

Owl puts the honey down and returns to the boat to collect the money

Pussycat It won't be so heavy when we've eaten some.

Owl Here's the money. (*He hands it to her*)

Pussycat Good. Very useful. (*She puts the money down behind the honey-pot*)

Owl On an island? I doubt if they use money here. (*In his normal voice*) I say.

Pussycat (*frightened*) What?

Owl What are we whispering for?

Pussycat I don't know.

Owl There's no-one here to wake up!

They sit down back to back on the honey-pot, then look around

Pussycat It's ever so dark.

Owl Don't worry about the dark. Ah, Pussy (*He puts a wing round her*), at last we're on our own.

A moving beam of light appears from off stage

Just you and I, and there are so . . .

Pussycat (*seeing the beam of light and jumping up*) Aaah.

Owl (*not realizing*) Don't worry, Pussy; there's no need to be frightened of the dark.

Pussycat It's not that. (*Pointing*) Look.

Owl Really, Pussy, you are . . . (*He sees the beam of light*) Aaah. Oh, oh, I say. (*He jumps up, his wings starting to flap, but he tries to be brave*) Just your imagination.

Pussycat Then why are your wings flapping? You know your wings only
flap when you're nervous.
Owl Well, I er—I'm not exactly nervous—just——

The noise of loud, bitter sobbing is heard from where the light is coming
(*Hearing the sobs*)—terrified! Let's move to the trees.

*They start to move in opposite directions. Realizing they are thus separated
they join hands and again start to go, but again in opposite directions. They
come together again and becoming more confused as the sobs from off stage
get louder, they cross each other and end up separated again. Owl hides
behind one set of Bong Trees, Pussycat behind the other*

DAVID WOOD and SHEILA RUSKIN

THE PRINCE, THE WOLF AND THE FIREBIRD

AFRON / MOUSHKA

Set in Russia, late 10th century. Princess Katatiana Henyanovna Momoushka —or just Moushka—can best be described as "an ageing damsel", desperate for a husband. Her three dolls, always with her, are known as "the girls"— Louki, Douki and Jouki. King Afron, a rather apprehensive man, also wishes to wed but had not bargained for such a bride. The scene is inside a palace— Moushka is veiled at first . . .

Afron (*scurrying to the door after him*) Ivan—don't go yet—I think I'm going to be . . .

Afron, in an agony, stares at Moushka. She is staring at where he has been standing. She gives a little cough

Moushka Shall we sit down?
Afron (*starts*) Yes.
Moushka Where are you?
Afron Here.
Mouska Oh. Where's the chair?
Afron There's only the throne.
Moushka That'll do. Bring it here.
Afron Yes, at once—my love. (*He gets it*) There.
Moushka Thank you. Will you hold the girls? (*She holds out Louki and Jouki*)
Afron (*understanding*) Ah—the girls. (*Suspiciously*) How old are you?
Moushka A lady never tells her age.
Afron You are old enough, are you? I mean . . . the one that's ready for marriage?
Moushka I'm quite ready, thank you.
Afron Wouldn't you like to take your . . . your hat off?
Moushka It is the custom in my country for a lady to be veiled while being proposed to.
Afron (*surprised* Is it really?
Moushka A lady never lies—off you go.
Afron Yes—(*He drops to one knee*) Your Royal Highness, I know this may come as a shock to you.
Moushka Yes—it has.
Afron But will you marry me?
Moushka Yes. (*She leans back into the throne*) Phew! Girls, we've made it. I'll now remove the hat. Are you holding onto something?
Afron (*nervously*) Yes. The girls.
Moushka I don't think they'll bear your weight. Hold onto the throne. (*He does so*) Now. (*She unveils*) There. Oh, you're ugly.

136

Afron *I'm* ugly! Ooh and for this I exchanged a fabulous beast.

Moushka It's no use crying over spilt milk.

Afron Ah—I've got it—it's the middle of the night. It's a nightmare. I shall wake up in a minute then FLOOM you'll go and disappear.

Moushka pinches him

Don't.

Moushka You're awake.

Afron Then it's a trick—you're not her. You can't be.

Moushka I am Princess Katatiana Henyanovna Pouska Mimoushka Boris's daughter.

Afron Where are my swords?

Moushka You wouldn't kill me?

Afron Not you, dear lady, myself.

Moushka If you dare kill yourself—I'll get Daddy to wage war on you— so there!

Afron You can't do that—I'm a defenceless man—I haven't got an army.

Moushka No army! Well, you must get one.

Afron Yes, I'll pop out for one tomorrow, dear lady.

Moushka You may call me Moushka.

Afron Moushka.

Moushka Now I've seen quite enough of the stables, thank you, let's go into your palace.

Afron This is the palace.

Moushka This is the . . . oh, how much can a lady take!

Afron I'm sorry. Perhaps you'd rather not go through with the marriage?

Moushka I've accepted it. I'm honour bound to go through with it.

Afron But if you don't like me and I don't like you it's lunacy to get married.

Moushka I do like you and you're a cruel wicked tall dark and ugly beast to say you don't like me. (*She weeps*) A lady's doing her best.

Afron Don't cry—please don't cry. I *do* like you—there. Now please stop. *Moushka weeps more*) Don't. You'll make me cry—I always cry when other people cry—I do like you—ooh— (*He weeps*) don't cry.

Moushka (*stopping a bit and hugging him*) Don't cry. I didn't mean to make you cry. There—wipe your eyes on the girls, they won't mind.

Afron Thank you.

Moushka No—I draw the line at blowing. We mustn't cry—this is supposed to be the happiest day of our life.

Afron Yes. Are you hungry?

Moushka Famished.

Afron Shall we go and boil some eggs?

Moushka Ask the cook to do it. I'm a little too fatigue.

Afron Do you speak French?

Moushka Perfectly.

Afron So do I—we can have conversations.

Moushka Let's ask cook to do the eggs first.

Afron (*archly*) Les oeufs!

Moushka (*lovingly*) Les oeufs!

Afron I'm afraid there isn't a cook, Moushka my love, she's left.

Moushka Then we must get another one.

Afron Well—that will be tricky—you see, we can't pay her. You might as well know, Moushka, you're marrying a pauper—I haven't a penny —just a few eggs.

Moushka Well, you might as well know you're marrying one of the richest ladies in the world—I'm heir to Daddy's throne, you see.

Afron I think I'm going to be . . .

Moushka Ugh—not on me. Go outside if you're going to be.

Afron It's all right—it's passing.

Moushka Good. And just to be going on with—we've got my dowry. My dowry! Neddy's got my dowry! Saddle the horses, we must catch them up.

Afron There aren't any horses . . .

Moushka Then run, you fool! (*She seizes his arm*)

Afron But I'm going to be . . .

Moushka There isn't time. (*She hauls him off*)

JACKSON LACY

RADIO RESCUE

SPARKY / JILL

Written in 1938, this play still fits into a more modern setting, although the idea of an unhappy orphanage is less common now. This dialogue takes place at the start of the play when Jill, and Sparky, a brother and sister, are planning to run away from the Millford Orphans Home. They are in the attic which is full of trunks and boxes. The play is American, but you could set it where you please.

Sparky enters stealthily; Jill follows and stumbles over a chair

Sparky What's the matter?
Jill I stumbled.

Sparky runs to window. Jill listens at door. Both stand still, then look at each other

Sparky (*after pause*) Nobody heard.
Jill It's the dormitory for the littlest ones below. They're all sound asleep.
Sparky Everybody is. Turn out that light in the hall.
Jill Turn on the light here first.

Sparky snaps it on. Jill turns out hall light. They are much more at ease. It is a single light hanging over spot where they set their radios. The rest of the room, including door, is in shadow

Sparky You hold the lid and I'll lift the radios. Here's the last tube. She'll work now! Put it in while I do the battery.

The children glow with excitement when they are settled in their places. Sparky takes package which is bulging from his pocket, hands it to Jill. She holds it. He gets another, which he sets on a trunk soon after entrance, for himself

Jill Are these the very last things we have to get?
Sparky The very last. Both sets ought to work tonight.
Jill Sparky!
Sparky Yeah?
Jill Are we really going to try them?
Sparky Soon as I get this wired up What you waiting for? You know how to put in a tube. I showed you twice.
Jill (*putting tube in*) How long will yours take?
Sparky About two minutes.
Jill I just can't wait.
Sparky We've waited two years. Guess we can wait two minutes more.
Jill It doesn't seem as if it was two years since we began saving for these.

139

Sparky I started on the aerial two years ago tonight. I know because it's my birthday. It's more'n a year since we got that receiving set.

Their conversation is punctuated by breaks due to intense concentration when something doesn't go quite right)

Jill We didn't think, that night, it would be a year before we could buy the last new tube for it.

Sparky We could have bought it before, of course, if (*Pause*) we hadn't had to buy the parts for the sending set.

Jill It's good you found that turned-in radio. We'd never have got done if you'd had to build them both.

Sparky It's more fun to build it, though. And it didn't take much longer. Even a second-hand one would cost more than this, and we'd have had to earn that much more money. (*Pause*) Anyway, it's no good without a license, and I had to learn on Billy's before I could get that.—There!

Jill Is it ready?

Sparky (*his voice shaking with excitement*) Yes. Is yours?

Jill Yes. Look and see if it's right.

Sparky (*Examining it with care*) You're pretty good for a girl. Now we'll try them.

Jill Hadn't we better wait till tomorrow? Miss Fetterling is going to New York, and we'll be sure not to be caught.

Sparky I couldn't wait another minute.

Jill (*pause*) I'm afraid!

Sparky Why, we've pounded and sawed and everything. No one ever heard.

Jill I didn't mean that.

Sparky What *did* you mean?

Jill What if they shouldn't work? I couldn't bear it!

Sparky (*getting up*) Of course they'll work. (*Boasting*) I've done everything exactly right.

Jill It seems sort of—magic.

Sparky It's only knowing how. And taking enough pains. (*Very proud*) My license is for the short wave band 6.3 millicycles. What'll we try?

Jill You choose.

Sparky (*gets book. Both pull up chairs and sit*) Well, you tune in and I'll call. (*Looks at Jill and sees window open*)

Jill My hand shakes.

Sparky Jill!

Jill What?

Sparky We forgot to cover the window. (*He runs to window, fastening blanket over it*)

Jill It's good you thought of that. Miss Fetterling's window is on this side. It's sure to be open. She's always talking about fresh air.

Sparky Her light's out.

Jill looks toward door—starts)

What's the matter?

Jill catches her breath and points to door. The light which sifts under it and through keyhole is wavering, now showing, now gone

Jill Look! There's a light in the hall.

The pencil of light that comes through keyhole vanishes entirely They tiptoe to door and listen. Light appears and vanishes again. Sparky puts his ear to keyhole. He nods at Jill and they tiptoe away

Sparky (*very low, lifting a radio*) Someone's listening at the keyhole. Help me put them away. (*Stealthily they place radios again in trunk*)
Jill We'd better hide. I'll get behind this trunk. (*She gets behind trunk*)
Sparky (*sitting on trunk*) No use. They'll know someone's here because of the light.
Jill Turn it off.
Sparky They'll see it go.
Jill Do you suppose it's the matron?
Sparky No. She'd come in.
Jill I know who it is—Martha. (*She climbs over trunk and sits on chair*) She knows we have a secret. She's been snooping around for weeks trying to find out what it is.
Sparky That's just like her.
Jill Let her listen as long as she likes. We'll just wait till she goes.
Sparky She won't go. She's seen the light. She's heard our voices. I'm going to open the door and catch her. (*Crosses toward door*)

Jill stops him

Jill Don't ever tell her. She can't keep a secret five minutes.
Sparky Course I won't tell her! She'd go straight and tattle to the matron. She's the meanest girl in the Home. We'll pretend we're reading those magazines. (*He takes a "Radio News" from a trunk-top*).

CHARLOTTE CHORPENNING

THE SHRIMP AND THE ANEMONE
EUSTACE / HILDA

Hilda and Eustace spend a good deal of time together, since the birth of a baby sister and their mother's death. Hilda is 12½, the older by nearly 4 years, and is over-concerned with her brother's morals, behaviour and well-being. She tends to dominate and manipulate him . . . the idea of an anemone sucking up a shrimp is used to open this novel. The scene takes place on a walk, and the consequences of it are to alter Eustace's life.

Time: 1905

Hilda There's Miss Fothergill and her companion.

Eustace Oh! Let's turn back!

Hilda Why should we turn back? It's just the opportunity we've been looking for.

Eustace Perhaps you have—I haven't.

Hilda The Bible says "Sick and in prison and I visited you". You've always been naughty about this Eustace. It's the chief failing I've never been able to cure you of.

Eustace But she's so ugly.

Hilda What difference does that make?

Eustace And she frightens me.

Hilda A big boy like you.

Eustace Her face is all crooked.

Hilda You haven't seen it. You always run away.

Eustace And her hands are all black.

Hilda Silly, that's only her gloves.

Eustace Yes, but they aren't proper hands, that's why she wears gloves. Annie told me.

Hilda She ought to have known better.

Eustace Anyway we've been told ever so often not to speak to strangers.

Hilda She isn't a stranger, she's always been here. And it doesn't matter as long as they're old and . . . ugly, and ill, like she is.

Eustace Perhaps she'll say "Go away, you cheeky little boy. I don't want to talk to you. You want to beg, I suppose?" What shall I do then?

Hilda Of course she wouldn't. Ill people are never rude. Besides she'll see me behind you.

Eustace But what shall I say to her?

Hilda You always find plenty to say to Nancy!

Eustace Oh, but I couldn't say those sort of things to her.

Hilda Well, say, "How do you do, Miss Fothergill? It's a nice day isn't it? I thought perhaps you would like me to push your bath chair.

Eustace But I might upset her. You know how I once upset baby in the pram.

142

Hilda Oh there wouldn't be any risk of that. Miss Fothergill's grown-up. You'll only just be able to move her. Then you could say, "Aren't I lucky to be able to walk?"

Eustace Oh no! She wouldn't like that!

Hilda Then think of something yourself.

Eustace But why don't you speak to her Hilda? Wouldn't that do as well? It would really be better, because if I speak to her she'll think you don't want to.

Hilda It doesn't matter about me, I want to see what good manners you've got.

Eustace But won't it be deceitful if I say "How do you do" without meaning it? She won't know I'm doing it to please you, and she'll think I'm politer than I really am. And Jesus will say I'm a whited sepulchre like in that sermon we heard last Sunday. Besides, we are told to do good by stealth, not out in the open air.

Hilda I don't think Jesus would mind. He always said we were to visit the sick and that meant whether we wanted to or not. Those ministering children Minny read to us about were good because they visited the poor, the book didn't say they wanted to.

Eustace You don't know that Miss Fothergill is poor. I don't think she can be, because she lives in that big house, you know, all by itself with lovely dark green bushes all round it. Jesus never said we were to visit the rich.

Hilda Now you're only arguing. You said that about Jesus and not being polite on purpose because you don't want to do your duty. It isn't as if you were doing it for gain . . . that would be wrong, of course.

Eustace Of course.

Hilda She might give you a chocolate though. Old ladies like that often have some.

Eustace I don't want her nasty chocolates.

Hilda There, I knew you'd say something naughty soon. Here she comes, if you speak to her now, she'll know you don't really want to, you look so cross, so you won't be deceiving her.

Eustace Oh, Hilda, I can't!

Hilda Oh, Eustace, please do it for my sake! Remember how I helped you with the toboggan yesterday, and how I always let you pat down the castles tho' I am a girl and I never mind playing horses with you, tho' Minny says I ought not to at my age . . . and how Aunt Sarah said you wouldn't be anywhere without me. And if you don't mind how I feel, just think of poor Miss Fothergill going home and saying to the housemaid, "I met such a dear little boy on the cliff this morning, he spoke to me so nicely, it's quite made me forget" . . . well, you know, her face and hands, and everything . . . "I think I shall ask him to tea and give him a lot of lovely cakes".

Eustace Oh, that would be dreadful! You wouldn't let me go? Promise, and I'll speak to her now. (*He goes to Miss Fothergill*)

Hilda I won't promise, but I'll see.

Eustace (*off*) Please, I wanted to say—How do you do, Miss Fothergill, isn't it a nice day?   L. P. HARTLEY

THE SILVER CURLEW

DOLL / TOM TIT TOT

The Norfolk version of Rumplestiltskin. Doll, the miller's daughter, is married to the King who believes she is a fine spinner. She is desperate to guess the name of the evil little creature who has helped her, before he can claim her baby

Doll Oh me, my baby! Oh me, oh me, oh me! Fair as the flax, blue as the flax-flower—and a record crop to spin. Whatever shall I do? Oh me, oh me! I'll never live to see your Christening-Day. (*She sings sobbingly*
  My white baby
  Smooth as a rose
  Smells so sweet
  From her head to her toes . . .

(*She breaks down and weeps*)

There is an ominous change of atmosphere as the fountain hisses and smokes and Tom Tit Tot leaps out of it

Tom Tit Tot What are yew cryin' for?
Doll (*sobbing mechanically*) None of your business. (*She looks up and gives a little scream*) I declare! If it isn't you.
Tom Tit Tot Yis, that's me. He, he, he! (*He twirls his tail*)
Doll What have you come for?
Tom Tit Tot Hoo! Hoo! Hoo! For yew, yew, yew! (*He twirls his tail*) The year is up, Doll Codling. Yar mine! Yar mine!
Doll Don't talk such nonsense.
Tom Tit Tot Yar mine, mine, mine.
Doll I'm nothing of the sort, Mister What's-your-name.
Tom Tit Tot (*crossing to the cradle*) What's-my-name, what's-my name? That's what yew doon't know, Doll Codling, that's what yew'll niver know till I've got yew safe and sound whar nobody'll niver set eyes on yew again. (*He bends over the cradle*) What's this yew've got here in the cradle, Doll Codling? So sure as I dew live, that'a little baby.
Doll (*snatching up the Baby*) Leave it be, you nasty sooty imp. Leave my baby be.
Tom Tit Tot Yar fond o' yar baby, are yew?
Doll That I am.
Tom Tit Tot Yew'll be sorry to leave that.
Doll That I would. (*To the Baby*) But I'm never going to leave you, am I, my precious?
Tom Tit Tot We'll see about that, Doll Codling. If yew doon't guess my name in nine, this instant minute, yew'll leave yar baby for iver and a day.

144

Doll You wouldn't have the heart.

Tom Tit Tot No, I would not have the heart. And for why? Becos I hain't got a heart, and yew can't not have what you hain't not got. (*He crosses to* L *of her*) He, he, he! Guess me in nine, or yar mine, mine, mine! Come now, what's my name? (*He moves in close to* L *of her*)

Doll (*sitting on the fountain*) That's Bill.

Tom Tit Tot Noo that hain't. Thar goos one. (*He twirls*)

Doll That's Ned.

Tom Tit Tot Noo that hain't. Thar goos two!

Doll Is that Mark?

Tom Tit Tot Noo that hain't. Thar goos three.

Doll Then that's Sammle.

Tom Tit Tot Noo that hain't. Thar goos four.

Doll A-well, is that Methusalem?

Tom Tit Tot 'Tain't that norther. Thar goos five.

Doll Then that must be Zebedee.

Tom Tit Tot 'Tain't, 'tain't, 'tain't. Thar goos six.

Doll (*anxiously*) I reckon that's Hasdrubal.

Tom Tit Tot Noo that hain't. Thar goos seven.

Doll (*frightened*) That's Nebuchadnezzar certain-sure.

Tom Tit Tot 'Tain't, 'tain't, 'tain't. Thar goes eight. One more, Doll Codling, yew've only one more guess.

Doll looks desperately around and notices the Book of Names

Doll (*triumphantly*) I know what that is.

Tom Tit Tot Noo yew doon't, noo yew doon't.

Doll I do, I do, I do. That's Nicodemus.

Tom Tit Tot He, he, he!
                    Thar goos nine!
                    Come along o' me,
                    Yar mine, mine, mine.
Say farewell to yar mammy, little baby. A pretty little baby, tew be sure. Say farewell to yar little baby, Doll.

Doll (*rising*) No, no, no, no, no.

Tom Tit Tot (*after a pause*) A-well, 'tis a pity tew part a baby from its mammy. I'll tell yew what I'll dew. I'll let yew bring yar little baby with yew.

Doll Bring my baby to the horrid place you live in!

Tom Tit Tot 'Tis a bewtiful place I live in, a bewtiful place. And yar baby's a bewtiful baby tew live in it. I like yar baby as much as I like yew. I'll tell yew what I'll dew. I'll give yew another night tew think it over, and tomorrow when I come agin yew shall have three more guesses at me, and if yew doon't guess me that time, yew and yar baby shall come tew me for iver.

Doll And if I do, you'll go away for ever?

Tom Tit Tot That's a bargain, Doll Codling.

Doll It's all or nothing, then, and that's a bargain. But . . . Oh, me!

Tom Tit Tot What's yar trouble now?

Doll Flax is my trouble. Today I must spin the flax-crop before nightfull, or off goes my noddle.

Tom Tit Tot I'll spin yar flax for yew, Doll, I'll spin yar flax. I won't lose my bargain for a thimbleful of spinning. But yew'd best come along o' me this instant minute.

Doll That I won't then. I'll neither come with you nor lose my noddle. I'm sure I shall guess you in three.

Tom Tit Tot Noo yew woon't, noo yew woon't. Nobody can't niver guess my name. Today I'll spin yar flax, and tomorrow yew an' yar baby shall be *mine*.

He jumps into the fountain and exits. The fountain hisses and smokes

Doll (*sitting on the fountain*) Tomorrow—you and me—will be his. (*She clasps the Baby to her and stares out front*)

ELEANOR FARJEON

SUMMER AND SMOKE

JOHN / ALMA

This scene opens a very adult play about the lives of a doctor and the woman who loved, but lost, him. Alma grows up to be a rather sad and lonely spinster with many problems. But here the prim small girl and the rather tough boy are still children, and their futures not known.

Time: the early years of this century.

Place: near the Angel of the Fountain in the Park

Alma aged 10 enters. She already has the dignity of a adult, a quality of delicacy and spirituality about her. She has a habit of cupping her hands, one under the other in a way similar to that of receiving Holy Communion. She stands in front of the stone angel a few moments, then bends to drink. John enters. He shoots a pea shooter at Alma's bent over back. She utters a cry and turns. He laughs

John Hi, preacher's daughter. I been looking for you.

Alma You have?

John Was it you that put them handkerchiefs on my desk? Answer up!

Alma I put a box of handkerchiefs on your desk.

John I figured it was you. What was the idea, Miss Priss?

Alma You needed them.

John Trying to make a fool of me?

Alma Oh, no.

John Then what was the idea?

Alma You have a bad cold and your nose has been running all week. It spoils your appearance.

John You don't have to look at me if you don't like my appearance?

Alma I like your appearance.

John Is that why you look at me all the time?

Alma I—I don't.

John Oh, yeh, you do. You been keepin' your eyes on me all the time. Every time I look around I see them cat eyes of yours looking at me. That was the trouble today when Miss Blanchard asked you where the River Amazon was. She asked you twice and you still didn't answer because you were lookin' at me. What's the idea? What've 'y' got on your mind anyhow? Answer up.

Alma I was only thinking how handsome you'd be if your face wasn't dirty. Because you don't use a handkerchief and you wipe your nose on the sleeve of that dirty old sweater.

John Hah!

Alma That's why I put the handkerchiefs on your desk and I wrapped them

147

up so nobody would know what they were. It isn't my fault that you opened the box in front of everybody!

John What did you think I'd do with a strange box on my desk? Just leave it there till it exploded or something? Sure I opened it up. I didn't expect to find no—*handkerchiefs* in it!

Alma I'm sorry that you were embarrassed. I honestly am awfully sorry that you were embarrassed . . . because I wouldn't embarrass you for the world.

John Don't flatter yourself that I was embarrassed. I don't embarrass that easy.

Alma It was stupid and cruel of those girls to laugh.

John Hah!

Alma They should all realize that you don't have a mother to take care of such things for you. It was a pleasure for me to be able to do something for you, only I didn't want you to know it was me who did it.

John (*thrusting the box at her*) Take 'em back.

Alma PLEASE keep them.

John What do I want with them? (*He tosses the box to ground and goes to the fountain to drink*) Does she have a name?

Alma Yes, I found out that she does. It's carved in the base, but it's all worn away so you can't work it out with your eyes.

John Then how do you know it?

Alma You have to read it with your fingers. I did and it gave me cold shivers. YOU read it and see if it doesn't give you cold shivers. Go on. Read it with your fingers. . . .

John Why don't you tell me and save me the trouble?

Alma I'm not going to tell you.

John grins, crouches, and runs his fingers over the base

John E?

Alma Yes, E is the first letter.

John T?

Alma Yes.

John E?

Alma E!

John K?

Alma No, no, not K . . . R!

John Eternity?

Alma ETERNITY! . . . Didn't it give you the cold shivers?

John Nahh!

Alma Well, it did me.

John Because you're a preacher's daughter. Eternity . . . What is eternity?

Alma (*in a hushed and wondering voice*) It's something that goes on and on when life and death and time and everything else is all through with.

John There's no such thing.

Alma There is. It's what people's souls live in when they have left their bodies. My name is Alma and Alma is Spanish for soul. Did you know that?

John Have you ever seen a dead person?

Alma No.

John I have. They made me go in the room when my mother was dying and she caught hold of my hand and wouldn't let me go . . . and so I screamed and hit her.

Alma Oh, you didn't do that!

John (*sombrely*) Uh-huh. She didn't look like my mother. Her face was all ugly and yellow and—terrible—bad smelling! And so I hit her to make her let go of my hand. They told me that I was a devil!

Alma You didn't know what you were doing.

John My dad is a doctor.

Alma I know.

John He wants to send me to college to study and be a doctor but I wouldn't be a doctor for the world. And have to go in a room and watch people dying! Jesus!

Alma You'll change your mind about that.

John Oh, no I won't. I'd rather BE a devil like they called me and go to South America on a boat . . . Give me one of them handkerchiefs. *Alma brings them, John takes one, damps it in the fountain and wipes his face* Is my face clean enough to suit you now?

Alma Yes! . . . Beautiful!

John WHAT??!!

Alma I said "Beautiful".

John Well . . . let's kiss each other. . . .

Alma turns away

Come on, let's just try it.

He seizes her shoulders, and gives her a quick rough kiss. She stands amazed one hand cupping the other. Voice of a child calling "Johnny, Johnny" . . . John snatches Alma's hair ribbon, and runs off with a mocking laugh. Hurt and bewildered Alma turns back to the stone angel for comfort. She crouches and touches the inscription with her fingers

TENNESSEE WILLIAMS

THURSDAY

BEE / THURSDAY

Bee has become caught up in the life of Thursday, the sullen lonely boy from her school. Although it is hard to get through to him she feels love and compassion for him—especially now when he has been missing for some days

Bee (*calling after Thursday*) Thursday! Thursday! Wait! It's all right, Thursday. It's only me. Thursday, it's me, Bee . . . Thursday, please. Please, please listen. I must ask you what's been happening. Why did you go like that? What have you been doing? Where have you been? Please, Thursday, you could tell me. If it's a secret, I won't tell, you know I won't. I'm safe. I'd never give you away. What is it? What's the matter? Won't you speak to me? Thursday . . . it's Bee. Have you forgotten?

Thursday (*mouthing the word*) Bee . . .

Bee Perhaps you've forgotten everything? If you've lost your memory you might not remember anything. I know you didn't give your real name where you were working. Is that what it is? Do you know who you are? Do you remember me? We're at school together, the Pottery Lane School. Your name is Thursday, you live in Soringhurst Terrace. The name of the mistress who takes our form is Miss Stevens. You do remember, don't you, Thursday? You do remember me? (*She steps forward and puts a hand on his arm*)

Thursday (*leaping back*) Don't touch me.

Bee Thursday!

Thursday Go away.

Bee You do know who I am? You haven't forgotten everything?

Thursday I haven't forgotten.

Bee What's the matter then? Why don't you want me?

Thursday I don't want anyone. I just want to be left alone.

Bee I know. I won't bother you, truly I won't. But it's so long since I've seen you and no-one knows where you are and I thought something awful must have happened.

Thursday Nothing's happened. I wanted to be alone, that's all.

Bee You could have told me you were going.

Thursday You'd have tried to get hold of me. I told you, I had to get away.

Bee Why? What's wrong?

Thursday (*flatly*) I'm perfectly all right.

Bee Where are you living then? . . . When will you come back?

Thursday I don't know if I shall come back.

Bee Never?

Thursday I shouldn't think so. There's nothing to come back for.

150

Bee (*quickly*) Not for me?

Thursday No.

Bee Don't go. Wait a minute. Even if you don't want me, there's something you ought to know. The police are looking for you. Because you're missing.

Thursday Who put them on to me? Was it you?

Bee Of course it wasn't.

Thursday I know who it was.

Bee Who?

Thursday I know. They're against me.

Bee Who's against you. Is it something to do with Molly?

Thursday She's probably in it too.

Bee Who else? Who's against you? Is it something to do with Molly?

Thursday She's probably in it too.

Bee Who else? Who's against you? Tell me, perhaps I could help.

Thursday No-one can help.

Bee I'd try. You know I'm not against you, don't you?

Thursday Aren't you?

Bee Who are they who're against you? Who's doing something against you? Please tell me.

Thursday You wouldn't understand.

Bee I might. Try.

Thursday It's too complicated. I can't explain.

Bee You don't want to.

Thursday No.

Bee Isn't there anything I can do to help?

Thursday No. Thank you. Only go away.

Bee What are you going to do?

Thursday That's nothing to do with you.

Bee It is. Please tell me.

Thursday I don't know. I never know what's going to happen. They decide.

Bee But who are they?

Thursday Sometimes it's one person, sometimes another. I can never be sure.

Bee Why should they stop you seeing me?

Thursday They don't. You're here aren't you?

Bee Don't you want to see me again?

Thursday No. You shouldn't cry. You look ugly when you cry. Go back. I just want to be left alone ... (*He starts to move off, then turns*) Bee! If they ask, say no-one need bother. I'm all right on my own. (*He goes*)

Bee Let me come too!

CATHERINE STORR

TITIAN

SALVATORE / LISA

This play is the author's idea of what might have occurred in the boyhood of the artist Titian (1477–1576) Tiziano Vecelli, a poor 10-year-old boy and Salvatore, the less talented 12-year-old son of a rich Lord of the Manor, Signor Zampanti, have entered a painting competition. It is to be judged by the great Bellini from Venice.

Both scenes take place in the medieval kitchen of a house in the village of Cadore, where Tiziano has hidden his painting behind a cover on the wall. Lisa and Caterina are younger sisters of the two boys

Two heads appear in the window almost immediately. They are Salvatore and Lisa

Lisa Is this the place?
Salvatore Yes. Come on, let's go in.

They go to the door and find it locked, then appear at the window again

Lisa Now what are you going to do?
Salvatore Climb in at the window, of course. (*He climbs in*)
Lisa What about me?
Salvatore Can't you climb in, too?
Lisa Not by myself. Come and help me.
Salvatore Girls are a nuisance. (*He helps her in*)
Lisa Was the door locked before? Did you always have to come in the window?
Salvatore No, it wasn't locked. Someone's been here since I was in last time. It was all dirty then and now it's clean.
Lisa Come on, then. Let me see your painting. I'm getting tired of hearing about the old thing.

Salvatore hands her the picture

Salvatore There! What do you think of it?
Lisa Not bad! Yes, there's the door and the cask by it. It looks all right to me, Salvatore.

She hands it back to him and he studies it, while Lisa goes to the fireplace and then to the little door

What's in here?
Salvatore A store-room and the back door of the house.
Lisa (*trying the door*) It's locked, and there isn't any key.
Salvatore (*looking at the cask near the fireplace*) Yes, there is a key. It was in the door the last time I saw it.

Lisa Then where is it now? It isn't here. There must be something precious hidden in there, or why would the door be locked?

Salvatore That's silly!

Lisa Is it silly? Wasn't the front door locked, too, and you said yourself that someone's been here?

Salvatore (*leaning on the cask as if he were about to lift it*) That's true.

Lisa What's wrong with you? What are you trying to do to the cask?

Salvatore It's in the wrong place. It's been pushed over here and it should be right over there. Help me to move it back to match the picture.

Lisa Move it yourself, lazy.

Salvatore Now, Lisa! All right then, you look at the picture while I move it and tell me when I've got it right.

Lisa takes the picture

How's that (*As he moves the cask*)

Lisa No, a little more to the right.

Salvatore (*moving to the* L) Is this right then?

Lisa No. That's the wrong way. I said right, not left.

Salvatore This is right!

Lisa Don't you know which is your right hand?

Salvatore This one? (*He indicates his right hand*)

Lisa Yes, stupid!

Salvatore (*moving cask* R) Now is it right?

Lisa Yes. Oh, look there on the floor where the cask was standing. (*Pointing to the stains made by the spilled paint*)

Salvatore What is it?

Lisa Look and see. What does it feel like?

Salvatore (*stooping and running his hand over the stain*) I can't tell what it is because it's soaked into the wood.

Lisa It's red enough—whatever it is. What could it be—something red and runny enough to soak into wood:

Salvatore Do you suppose it's blood?

Lisa Oh-h-h——

Salvatore Do you suppose there's been a murder?

Lisa In here?

Salvatore Yes. (*He backs toward wall near door and knocks down key*) Oh, what was that?

Lisa The key. Look!

Salvatore The store-room key! Something funny's been going on here.

Lisa Aren't you afraid!

Salvatore fiddles around with the lock

Then why don't you open the door?

Salvatore The key sticks.

Lisa Here, let me try it. (*She turns the key*) There!

Salvatore hesitates

Why don't you go in?

He peeks in fearfully. Just as he is about to enter Lisa says 'Boo.''

Salvatore Lisa! Don't do that. (*He enters*) The place is full of paint.
Lisa Paint!
Salvatore Yes—blue, green, yellow and red. (*He comes running out with a jar of red paint which he puts on top of the cask while he stoops down and examines the stain on the floor again*) Aw—this isn't blood. It's paint. (*Standing up again*) Somebody's been painting here.
Lisa Who do you suppose it was?
Salvatore I don't know.
Lisa And what's he been painting? It must have been a picture, but I don't see any. Do you?
Salvatore It must be hidden. Whoever's been doing the painting hid his paints. He hid what he painted too.
Lisa There isn't any place to hide it in this room.
Salvatore There may be a secret panel or something.
Lisa A secret panel in a plastered wall? How funny you are, Salvatore.
Salvatore Let's look and see, anyway.

Both feel about quickly. Salvatore finally gets on the platform. He feels the cover

Salvatore Lisa!
Lisa It's loose.

Both pull it back enough to see, but the audience can not

How beautiful. This *is* a picture! See the Baby and the flowers! I wonder who could have painted it?
Salvatore Nobody that lives in Cadore. I know that. Even I couldn't do anything like this. It's some great artist! Maybe it's the great master Bellini, making it to give to Cadore!
Lisa And we're the first to find it out! Wait! There's a name here. Is it Bellini?
Salvatore Can you read it?
Lisa It's very scrawly. I can't make it out. Can you?
Salvatore It's all mixed up in the flowers. Why didn't he put it so it could be seen easily the way I have mine?
Lisa Look—there's a T-i-
Salvatore Z-i-a-
Lisa N-o. That's T-i-z-i-a-n-o—Tiziano! Is that Bellini's first name?
Salvatore I don't know, but it must be if he's put it here. Here's the other. V-e-c- That's not the way you spell Bellini. What is it? What is it, Lisa?
Lisa E-l-l-i-. What is that? Vecelli?
Salvatore Tiziano Vecelli? Tiziano—oh no! No!
Lisa It's his name. He couldn't make a picture like this.
Salvatore Oh, couldn't he? He's done it, hasn't he? But it won't do him any good. He won't win the prize. He won't! He won't! (*He dashes out from the cover like a wild thing and looks all about for something with which to ruin the painting*) I'll stop that!

Laughter outside

NORA TULLY

TITIAN

TIZIANO / CATARINA

Tiziano Catarina! Catarina!
Catarina What is it? Oh, what is it, Tiziano?
Tiziano My picture! My beautiful picture!

Catarina drops the flowers and comes running. Tiziano holds up the end of cover. She stands speechless with horror. Tiziano drops the cover

Catarina Who could have done such a wicked thing?
Tiziano I don't know.
Catarina You didn't tell anyone about your picture, did you?
Tiziano No, of course not.
Catarina Then somebody must have been watching you.
Tiziano I suppose so.
Catarina But who? Who would be likely to come this way? What would anyone be doing in this old house?
Tiziano I don't know, but it doesn't matter. I can't show my picture now. The great master will never know how I love to paint. I'll never go to Venice.
Catarina Oh—Tiziano—and your picture is so beautiful.
Tiziano I know it.
Catarina Can't you show it anyway?
Tiziano (*astoundedly*) No!
Catarina But why not? Please let me go for the master.
Tiziano No, Catarina—no. I don't even want to see it myself.
Catarina Oh, Tiziano, after all this work. Can't you do something about it? Can't you paint the flowers over again? You could paint it while I go for the master.
Tiziano Yes, I could. See, it could be covered with fresh paint and hardly noticed. The red here is dulled. I'll put blue over that—like violet in shadow.
Catarina And the yellow is dirty, too.
Tiziano Blue over that will make it look like dark green leaves. Quick, Rina, get me the paint.
Catarina The blue?
Tiziano And the red, too.
Catarina Then give me the key.
Tiziano (*running to the door*) It's gone!
Catarina Look! It's in the door! (*She tries the handle*) It's open.
Tiziano (*pushing her aside and rushing in*) Oh——
Catarina What's wrong?
Tiziano The paints! They're all gone. I can't do the flowers over again.

155

Catarina Oh, who could have done it? I think we ought to tell Father Anton about this. He'd find out who it was.

Tiziano We're not going to tell anybody. I don't want to know who did it.

Catarina I do!

Tiziano I couldn't bear to know.

Catarina I could. I'd like to find out who he is—and do something about it. That's what I'd like. You would, too. You know you would.

Tiziano No! No! I'd run if I saw him coming'

Catarina Why?

Tiziano I don't know. I couldn't bear to look at him. It's too horrible for anyone to do. It doesn't seem so real while I don't see him.

Catariana You wouldn't want him to see how much you cared.

Tiziano Oh—it doesn't matter who sees. I do care—I do.

Catarina I'm sorry, Tiziano. Then you're not going to do anything about it at all?

Tiziano No.

Catarina Then you are a silly, foolish boy, even if you are my own brother. Besides, I think it's wrong, what you're doing. Somebody did a bad thing and should be punished.

Tiziano Oh—Catarina. What's the use of punishing him?

Catarina If he were punished he wouldn't do bad things like that again.

Tiziano Yes, he would. He's that kind. He'd just be more careful not to be caught next time.

Catarina It would make me glad to see him sorry for what he's done.

Tiziano What good will that do? It wouldn't make my picture right.

Catarina Do you suppose it was a man or boy who did it?

Tiziano I don't know.

Catarina May I look at the picture again?

Tiziano If you want to.

Catarina looks and discovers the print of a child's hand on the painting. She puts her own beside it

Catarina It wasn't a man. It was somebody our size. The print of his hand is right here. It wasn't Tonio. He wouldn't do such a thing. Tiziano —could it be Salvatore?

Tiziano He'd do it. It's like him.

Catarina I'm going for Father Anton.

Tiziano No, don't. You mustn't.

Catarina Why not?

Tiziano We wouldn't dare tell on Salvatore. The Signor Zampanti would do terrible things to Father.

Catarina Oh—yes, he would. You painted on his doublet, too.

Tiziano Come along.

Caratina What are you going to do?

Tiziano What is there to do? I don't want to stay here.

Catarina Where are you going?

Tiziano Anywhere! Anywhere that isn't here!

Catarina Do you care if I stay here?

Tiziano What for?

Catarina Well, I've heard that sometimes when a person's done something bad, he comes back to see the place. If I stayed, I might find out something.

Tiziano What's the use of finding out? Come with me.

Catarina Hear them! Everyone is happy. They're shouting for Bellini.

Tiziano (*listening in despair, then lifting his face, another feeling dawning*) The great Bellini! I can see him, at least. I can look into his face. I can hear his voice. I'm going to find him, Catarina. I'm going to shout for him, too. He'll never see my picture, but there's something I'm going to give him. Stay if you like. But don't forget your promise to the Madonna.

He exits

Catarina begins to look about for clues. She looks out of the window and sees Zampanti and Salvatore coming and decides to hide. She tries to get in the store-room. It is locked so she finally climbs into the cask by the fireplace—just in time.

NORA TULLY

TOM'S MIDNIGHT GARDEN

TOM / HATTY

While Tom is staying with his Aunt and Uncle, after an illness, he meets at night-time Hatty, a mischievous temperamental and charming girl. Much later on in the book it is revealed that he has been entering the dreams of old Mrs Bartholomew upstairs as she relives her childhood. She is Hatty. Set in the present time and at the end of the nineteenth century

Hatty is singing while she and Tom build their tree house

Hatty "Her ghost wheels her barrow
  Thro' streets broad and narrow,
  Singing cockles and mussels
  Alive . . . alive . . . Oh!"

She continues humming the tune

Tom (*suddenly*) What's it like? I mean, I wonder what it's like to be a ghost?

Hatty stops singing and looks at Tom and laughs

  What is it like to be a ghost?
Hatty Like? . . . Ah, tell me, Tom.
Tom I'm not a ghost!
Hatty Don't be silly Tom. You forget that I saw you go right through the orchard door when it was shut.
Tom That proves what I say! I'm not a ghost but the orchard door is, and that was why I could go through it. The door's a ghost, and the garden's a ghost and so are you too!
Hatty Indeed I'm not! you are. You're a silly little boy! And you make a silly little ghost! Why do you think you wear those clothes of yours? None of my cousins ever played in the garden in clothes like that. Such outdoor clothes can't belong to nowadays, I know. Such clothes!
Tom They're my pyjamas! My best visiting pyjamas! I sleep in them! And this is my bedroom slipper!
Hatty And you go about so, in the daytime, always in your night clothes! And it's the fashion nowadays, is it, to wear only one slipper? Really you are silly to give such excuses! You wear strange clothes that no-one wears nowadays, because you're a ghost. Why! I'm the only person in the garden who sees you! I can see a ghost.
Tom Do you know I could put my hand through you . . . now . . . just as if you weren't there! . . .

Hatty laughs

  I could—I could!

Hatty You're a ghost!

Tom hits out at Hatty, and catches her wrist. She snatches her wrist back and nurses it

Your hand didn't go through my wrist; my wrist went through your hand! You're a ghost, with a cruel, ghostly hand!

Tom (*shouting*) Do you hear me? You're a ghost and I've proved it! You're dead and gone and a ghost!

There is a silence, then Hatty begins to weep

Hatty I'm not dead—oh, please, Tom, I'm not dead!

Tom All right then, Hatty! You're not a ghost. I take it all back—all of it. Only don't cry! (*She stops. They begin to play again*) Mind you, I'm not a ghost either!

Hatty does not reply

PHILIPPA PEARCE

THE TREASURE QUEST

ALICIA / SEBASTIAN

This exciting play was written for the Theatre In Education company at Watford Palace Theatre. Twenty years earlier Sebastian's father was captured and enslaved by Spaniards under the rule of Juan Carlos. Now Sebastian has arrived in England, by ship, with a message for Queen Elizabeth I and he meets Alicia who determines to help him. They discover that the cruel and scheming Lady Mary, a close friend of Alicia's widower father, has often visited Carlos in Spain. She tries to prevent the young people from finding a message buried on board the ship, but with the help of Pinch, a magic lobster, they triumph over her

As the scene opens Alicia and Sebastian are tied back to back

Alicia What happened?

Sebastian I don't know—there was a flash.

Alicia Just like before.

Sebastian And then. . . .

Alicia And then—I can't remember any more . . .

Sebastian But they've gone.

Alicia Who? Oh—you mean Lady Mary and Thomas. Where are they?

Sebastian I don't know—but we must be careful—they may be hiding.

Alicia What can we do?

Sebastian The first thing is to get free. Alicia, you said that Thomas did not bind you too tightly. Can you reach into the back of my jacket?

Alicia You jacket? Why?

Sebastian I have a dagger there. It was my only protection. If you can reach it you can cut our bonds.

Alicia I am trying.

Sebastian A little further—hurry, Alicia—we must find the proof before either your father returns or the Lady Mary interferes again.

Alicia I almost have it. There it is free.

Sebastian Right—now pass it to me.

Alicia Take care—do not cut yourself.

Sebastian Do not worry. I'll take care. It's coming.

Alicia But Sebastian—even if we do manage to escape—what are we going to do?

Sebastian Search for the treasure. Don't you see? You were right. The ring must be the key. Hold steady now. I'm nearly through the rope. There—now our hands and arms are free. Quickly—untie your legs.

Alicia But the Lady Mary and Thomas. Supposing they are near?

Sebastian I do not think so. With all the noise we've made we should have seen them by now. Right. Let's look for the treasure.

160

By this time both are free. They massage their limbs and they search

Alicia Sebastian—let me see the ring again so that I know what it is that I'm searching for.

Sebastian Here. The pattern is most distinctive. He said it was the key. It must fit into some part of the ship. . . .

Alicia But it's so small we'll never find it.

Sebastian Don't give up now. Keep on looking. (*He goes up the steps to the prow*)

Alicia (*going to the trap*) It's the wrong place. Oh, Sebastian—I knew it wouldn't work. We'll never find it.

Sebastian Don't give up now Alicia. Your father will be back soon and we must have proof.

They continue to search. Sebastian attempts to tear down planks, Alicia searches more quietly

Alicia Sebastian—I've found it! I'm sure I'm right this time. Look at the engraving—it's the same.

Sebastian I think you're right. Here, let me try . . . it gives a little . . . it fits!

Alicia Turn it Sebastian, turn it!

Sebastian I'm trying . . . it's giving . . . it's turning . . . Alicia! You're right. (*He turns the ring in the lock and lifts a plank*)

Alicia Sebastian . . . have we found the treasure?

Sebastian Yes . . . look at this. (*He pulls back the plank, and reveals a sword, set with jewels, which he removes and holds in front of himself*)

Alicia The treasure!

Sebastian Yes. It must be priceless. Feel the weight—it's solid gold!

Alicia And look at the jewels—diamonds, rubies, pearls . . .

Sebastian I wonder what else it holds?

Alicia What do you mean?

Sebastian It must reveal its secret. Remember it has a message of the utmost importance . . .

Alicia Of course . . . I forgot. (*Looking at the hilt*) Look here—the same engraving as on the ring . . .

Sebastian Then it must act as a key as before.

Sebastian inserts the key into the handle. At once the sword opens and it is possible to remove a piece of parchment within it

Sebastian Look, Alicia! Look! My father's message . . . for the Queen!

Alicia But what does it say?

Sebastian The invasion plans . . . but more than that . . . there is a list of agents; Sir Giles Abercrombie, Celia Blake. . . .

Alicia But is Lady Mary's name on the list?

Sebastian Sir Frederick Fitzemplar, Harriet Grading . . . Lady Mary Granville . . . Alicia, here we have the proof. . . . (*They hear voices off*)

Alicia Here comes my father. All we need to do is to show him the sword and the list. . . .

Sebastian He may still not believe us.

Alicia But we have proof!

Sebastian He may think that I am an imposter . . . with forged evidence . . .

Alicia No!—if he doubts at first we will convince him. He'll be so pleased
to think that your father is still alive.

HILARY CLULOW

MADE AND PRINTED IN GREAT BRITAIN BY
LATIMER TREND & COMPANY LTD PLYMOUTH
MADE IN ENGLAND